RECENT ADVANCES IN
ANIMAL NUTRITION — 2015

Recent Advances in Animal Nutrition

2015

P.C. Garnsworthy, PhD
J. Wiseman, PhD
University of Nottingham

Context Products Ltd
53 Mill Street, Packington
Leicestershire, LE65 1WN, United Kingdom

www.contextbookshop.com

First published 2019

British Library Cataloguing in Publication Data
Recent Advances in Animal Nutrition - 2015

ISBN 9781899043804
ISSN 0269-5642

Disclaimer

Preface

The 47th University of Nottingham Feed Conference was held at the School of Biosciences, Sutton Bonington Campus, 23rd – 24th June 2015. The Conference was divided into four sessions that covered areas of topical interest to the animal feed industry. These sessions were Ruminants, Microbiomes, General Issues, and Non-Ruminants.

The Ruminant section is concerned with improving health and performance of ruminant animals. The first chapter discusses effects of negative energy balance on health and reproduction. The second reports the benefits of allocating concentrates individually to grazing cows. The third chapter discusses assessment of mineral availability. The fourth chapter describes a range of techniques for monitoring metabolic health. The fifth chapter reviews effects of essential oils on rumen fermentation.

The Microbiome section contains two chapters that review recent advances in study of the rumen microbiome, and the gut microbiome in non-ruminants.

The General section starts with a chapter on the increasing demand for food as the population increases. The second forecasts the developments in livestock production in China.

The Non-Ruminant section is concerned with nutrition of pigs and aquaculture, and future trends in the pig industry. The first chapter provides an update on the benefits of n-3 fatty acids on reproduction in the pig. The second describes novel techniques for producing plants that can replace fish oil in aquaculture feeds. The third reviews use of fermented feeds for pigs. The fourth looks at developments in pig genetics and forecasts what type of pigs will be produced in 2025. The final chapter provides an overview of trends and opportunities in the pig feed market and supply trade.

We would like to thank all speakers for their presentations and written papers, which have maintained the high standards and international standing of the Nottingham Feed Conference. Unfortunately some speakers were unable to supply full written papers, so their summaries are provided for the proceedings. We are grateful to all those members of the feed industry who provided suggestions and assistance in developing the conference programme. We would also like to acknowledge the administrative (managed by Sheila Northover and Kathy Lawson), catering and support staff who ensure the smooth running of the conference. Finally we would like to thank the delegates who made valuable contributions both to the discussion sessions and the general atmosphere of the meeting.

P.C. Garnsworthy
J. Wiseman

Sponsors

The University of Nottingham is grateful to the following organisations for sponsoring the 47th Nottingham Feed Conference

CONTENTS

1

Effects Of Negative Energy Balance And Inflammation On The Reproductive Tract In Dairy Cows

H. BOLLWEIN

Clinic of Reproductive Medicine, Vetsuisse-Faculty, University of Zurich

Fertility is affected by negative energy balance (NEB) as well as by health status of the cow during early lactation – importantly, these factors interact with each other. Both factors affect ovarian activity as well as uterine involution after parturition.

Effects on the ovaries

The duration between parturition and resumption of luteal activity is related to the extent of the NEB in the first weeks of lactation. Cows with a more pronounced NEB between the first and second week postpartum ovulate later compared to cows with a moderate NEB. The decrease of dry matter intake towards the end of pregnancy and the homeorrhetic changes typical during the onset of lactation provoke an uncoupling of the somatotropic axis characterized by low IGF-I-concentrations irrespective of increased growth hormone (GH) secretion from the pituitary gland. IGF-I is well-known as a sensitive signal between metabolism, NEB and reproduction. Cows developing production diseases post partum exhibit significantly lower IGF-I concentrations several weeks before calving compared to cows remaining healthy in the transition period.

Low plasma glucose concentrations are frequently found in recently calved cows due to the high glucose demand of the mammary gland to support milk synthesis while elevated plasma NEFA concentrations reflect peripheral lipolysis. Serum concentrations of these metabolites are also reflected in the follicular fluid of the dominant follicle. *In vitro* studies showed that NEFAs have negative effects on the quality of oocytes, cumulus cells, and resultant blastocysts. In fact, higher plasma NEFA concentrations during the peripartum period are associated with delayed ovulation in postpartum dairy cows. Therefore, postpartal changes of serum concentrations of these metabolites alter the pattern of ovarian follicle growth and development, resulting in reduced reproductive performance in dairy cows.

High yielding dairy cows experiencing pronounced NEB during the transition period do not only exhibit a prolonged period of anoestrus. Remarkably, even when these cows initiate oestrous cycles following a period of anovulation or anoestrus, conception rate is compromised. Lack of P4 and lower concentrations of E2 during proestrus in the oestrous cycle preceding AI might result in shortened oestrous cycles due to premature luteal regression. According to the hypothesis of Britt damage to primary follicles induced by a NEB during the first weeks after parturition may cause disturbances of the ovulatory follicles developing around 60 to 80 days later. Such follicles may contain oocytes of lower quality and a reduced capacity to synthesize steroid hormones. These disturbances could be another reason for lower conception rates in cows exhibiting a NEB during the transition period.

Follicular activity in postpartum dairy cows is affected not only by metabolites and hormones, but also by inflammatory mediators. Metritis and mastitis are considered to be the most common infectious diseases during the postpartum period. Within three weeks after parturition, up to 40% of cows develop metritis and mastitis is found in approximately 20–50% of all dairy cows. Infectious diseases often perturb normal ovarian cyclic activity, resulting in abnormal folliculogenesis, development of cystic ovarian follicles or prolonged anoestrus. In cows with metritis the first postpartum dominant follicle had both reduced growth and peripheral plasma E2 were found to be lower. Escherichia coli (*E. coli*) is an important infectious agent causing metritis and mastitis. Much of the tissue pathology is associated with endotoxins from gram-negative bacteria, the lipopolysaccharides (LPS). LPS has been detected in plasma, uterine fluid, and follicular fluid of cows with metritis and in the plasma and milk of cows with *E. coli* mastitis. It has been reported that LPS acts at the either hypothalamus or pituitary gland to suppress gonadotrophin release and perturb follicle growth and function. Moreover, LPS is assumed to have a direct effect on the ovary, including follicular components such as the theca and granulosa cells and the oocyte.

Metabolic and inflammatory triggers do not only affect ovarian follicles during the puerperal period in the cow, but also ovarian activity in the developing foetus. A research group in Ireland studied the effect of restrictive feeding of pregnant cows (60% of their maintenance energy requirements shortly before conception until the end of the third month of pregnancy). Although birth weight of the offspring was unaltered, antral follicle number in calves born from restrictively fed dams were 60% lower compared with calves born from controls. Cows with a higher number of antral follicles show higher pregnancy rates, a shorter calving to conception interval and fewer services during the breeding season compared with cows with a low number of antral follicles. Thus, the results of this experiment provide evidence that maternal NEB during pregnancy may have an important trans-generational impact on the size of the ovarian reserve and thereby the fertility of the offspring.

The same research group examined the effects of mastitis occurring during pregnancy on ovarian development of their offspring and observed that dairy cows with a high number of somatic cells in the milk (>200 000 cells/ml) several (4 or 5) times during pregnancy gave birth to female calves with relatively low circulating concentrations of anti-Müllerian hormone (AMH) as adults. Anti-Müllerian hormone is produced exclusively by granulosa cells of healthy growing follicles and circulating AMH concentrations are highly correlated with the number of antral follicles and the size of the ovarian reserve in cattle and other species. Therefore, these results indicate that chronic infections during pregnancy of dairy cows diminish the size of the ovarian reserve, with potentially negative effects on the future reproductive performance in their offspring.

In the last five decades the percentage of cows that have been observed in oestrus and stand to be mounted has declined and duration of oestrus has reduced. A possible reason is reduced E2 concentrations as a result of a higher metabolism of this hormone. Lactating cows have higher liver blood flow and increased metabolic clearance of E2 compared to non-lactating cows. Another reason may be lower IGF-I levels in high yielding dairy cows. Production diseases also have a negative effect on oestrus behaviour. For example lame cows may be unable to mount herdmates. However, other production diseases such as mastitis induce acute as well as chronic stressors which affect the hypothalamus-pituitary-adrenal gland axis and the hypothalamus-pituitary-ovarian axis. Hence, GnRH and LH pulse frequency are reduced leading to short–term decreases in follicular E2 production, as well as delaying and reducing the magnitude of the LH surge.

Progesterone has a key role in reproductive performance, especially during pregnancy. For example, in the oestrous cycle preceding insemination low systemic P4 concentrations are detrimental to conception rate. Although not all mechanisms are understood, it is well known that pulsatile release of GnRH and thus of LH is suppressed by P4. Frequency of LH pulses has a significant influence on the dominant follicle. If P4 concentrations are high, LH pulse frequency is low and the dominant follicle undergoes atresia during dioestrus. In contrast, if P4 values are low during dioestrus, LH pulse frequency is higher. This increase in LH never reaches follicular-phase-type frequencies that are necessary for the final maturation of the preovulatory follicle and ovulation, and the dominant follicles show a longer persistence. Cows with follicles persisting more than four days have lower pregnancy rates.

After insemination, the postovulatory P4 rise between days 4 and 7 is important. P4 alters secretion of histotrophs by the endometrium enhancing the growth and development of the embryo. Thus, cows with a steep increase in P4 concentrations between days 4 and 7 after insemination have a greater chance of maintaining a pregnancy than animals with a delayed rise.

Synthesis of P4 by the CL can be affected by several mechanisms, especially by disturbances during the previous oestrous cycle. A smaller ovulatory follicle develops a smaller CL which synthetizes lower amounts of P4. Another reason is a higher metabolism of P4. Like E2, P4 is metabolized in the liver. Therefore, the increased feed intake and hepatic blood flow of high yielding dairy cows results in an elevated clearance of P4 and thereby lower peripheral P4 concentrations. Thus, negative correlations exist between P4 concentrations in the blood during the luteal phase and milk yield, as well as dry matter intake.

P4 concentrations in dairy cows can also be negatively affected by inflammatory diseases. For example, cows with severe bacterial uterine contamination have smaller CLs and lower P4 concentrations than healthy cows. The pathogenesis of luteal impairment caused by metritis is unclear. Metritis is accompanied by increased $PGF_{2\alpha}$ plasma concentrations, which possibly disturb luteal development. Other inflammatory mediators, such as tumor necrosis factor-α, which may be released during metritis, are cytotoxic to luteal cells. Furthermore, endotoxin inhibits responsiveness of the pituitary gland to GnRH, which could affect luteal development.

Persistent CLs are frequently found in cows suffering from metritis. Persistent CL is one of the most frequent abnormal ovarian activities in dairy cows, with a prevalence of 11 to 35%. Although pathogenesis of a persistent CL is not clearly understood, the luteotropic prostaglandin, PGE, which is elevated in cows showing uterine inflammation, might be involved. The impact of persistent CLs on bovine fertility is largely unknown. Some authors found no difference in reproductive competence between cows with persistent CL and normal cyclic cows, another study showed that persistent CLs were followed by a higher level of late embryonic and early foetal mortality. In our own study we reduced the prevalence of persistent CLs by an exogenous injection of $PGF_{2\alpha}$ in cows showing a CL five weeks after parturition. This treatment led to a significant increase in first service conception rate, a decrease in AI per conception ratio and a shortened calving-to-conception interval.

It is a widely accepted hypothesis that elevated $PGF_{2\alpha}$ synthesis induced by inflammatory diseases may be responsible for higher embryonic loss rate in pregnant cows. Cows affected by clinical mastitis between first AI and pregnancy require more inseminations and have a longer calving-to-conception interval compared to healthy cows. The inflammation-related induction of complete luteolysis was responsible for termination of pregnancy. However, in further experimental studies a single intravenous administration of LPS between days 7–9 of the oestrous cycle caused only a transient decrease of luteal size and P4 concentrations. Although the cows infused with LPS showed lower P4 values for some days compared to untreated control cows, the duration of the oestrous cycle was not significantly altered.

Effects on uterine involution

Uterine involution during the puerperal period is an important and critical process in the reproductive cycle of dairy cows. It includes reduction of uterine size, elimination of bacterial contamination and regeneration of the endometrium representing preconditions for a subsequent pregnancy. Cows suffering from uterine diseases due to disturbances of uterine involution show a calving-to-conception interval approximately 19 days longer and a 20% lower conception rate to first service compared to controls. Even after clinical resolution of a uterine infection, conception rates remain about 20% lower in affected cows. Finally, 3% of such cows remain infertile and have to be culled.

The main issues affecting uterine involution during the puerperium are retained placenta and uterine infections, mostly associated with peripartal complications such as dystocia, twins or stillbirths. Dystocia is usually associated with human obstetrical assistance resulting in an increased contamination of the uterus and vagina. A retained placenta contributes to the pathogenesis of metritis by providing an ideal environment for bacterial growth, due to the large amount of necrotic tissue present, the delay of lochia expulsion, and potential lesions to the uterus because of manual removal. Thus, bacterial uterine inflammation is a common consequence. However, during the first days after parturition the uterus is contaminated with a wide range of bacteria in nearly all cows. The development of metritis is dependent on the balance between immunity of the cow and pathogenicity of the bacteria.

There are conflicting results concerning effects of metabolites and production diseases on uterine involution. LeBlanc concluded that NEB contributes to immune dysfunction, a major factor in the establishment of reproductive tract inflammatory disease. High serum concentrations of ß-hydroxybutyrate (BHBA) and NEFA reduce the activity of polymorphonuclear neutrophils (PMN), which have an important role in uterine immune defence and are involved in the pathophysiology of metritis.

Hypocalcaemia causes a reduced uterine muscle tone, which could be responsible for retained placenta and a delay in uterine involution. Low blood calcium levels may also be associated with impaired immune function, but its association with uterine diseases is equivocal.

Some studies demonstrated that a short postpartum anovulatory period is associated with improved fertility, whereas others reported reduced fertility or did not find any effect. Studies used either oestrogens or GnRH analogues for postpartum suppression of ovulation. However, whether and to what extent uterine effects were caused indirectly by either suppression of ovulation or directly by the administered hormones, is not known. Oestrogens have a positive effect on myometrial contractility and enhance uterine immune response, whereas P4 induces a relaxation of uterine muscles and suppresses immunity. GnRH analogues also enhance uterine motility.

In one study we inhibited ovulation during puerperium in healthy dairy cows and in cows with postpartum uterine disease without hormonal treatments by repeated transvaginal follicular punctures. Suppression of ovulation by transvaginal follicular punctures had a positive effect on uterine involution especially in cows with uterine disease. This supports the suggestion that postpartum suppression of ovulation, and thus delayed secretion of P4, enhances the reduction in uterine size and the elimination of inflammation and bacterial contamination. These findings advocate against early induction of ovulation in cows with postpartum uterine disease.

Conclusion

Reduced fertility in dairy cows is not an inevitable consequence of high milk yield. Instead, production diseases, as well as infertility, may be caused by a variety of factors including the consequence of an insufficient adaptation capacity of affected cows to cope with the metabolic challenge during the transition period. Both, metabolic disorders and inflammatory processes have multifarious negative impacts on the onset of ovarian activity after parturition, uterine involution and oestrous behavior. Research has focused mainly on effects of either NEB or production diseases on reproductive function. In future, more investigations should be performed to understand what happens to the reproductive system in cows experiencing NEB while suffering from a production disease at the same time. Moreover, there is a lack of knowledge about the influence of robustness in dairy cows. Many high-yielding dairy cows remain healthy and fertile resulting in longevity. The differences and influence of the metabolic constellation contributing to fertility between higher yielding and lower yielding cows need specific attention and further clarification.

2

Concentrate Feeding Strategies For Individual Grazing Cows

J.L. HILLS[1], W.J. WALES[2] I.J. LEAN[3] S. C. GARCIA[4] J.R. ROCHE[5] AND F.R. DUNSHEA[6]

[1] *The University of Tasmania, Burnie, Tasmania 7320, Australia;*

[2] *Department of Department of Economic Development, Jobs, Transport and Resources, Ellinbank, Victoria 3821, Australia;*

[3] *SBScibus, Camden, New South Wales 2570, Australia;*

[4] *The University of Sydney, Camden, New South Wales 2570, Australia;*

[5] *DairyNZ, Private Bag 3221, Hamilton 3240, New Zealand;*

[6] *The University of Melbourne, Parkville, Victoria 3010, Australia.*

Summary

In pasture-based dairy systems, supplementary feeds are used to increase dry matter intake and milk production. Historically, supplementation involved the provision of the same amount of feed (usually a grain-based concentrate feed) to each cow in the herd during milking (i.e., flat-rate feeding). However, the availability of computerized feeding and milk monitoring technology has led to increased interest in the potential benefits of individually feeding cows different amounts and types of supplements according to one or more parameters (e.g., breeding value for milk yield, current milk yield, days in milk, body condition score, reproduction status, parity). In this mini-review, we consider the likely benefits of individualized supplementary feeding strategies for pasture-based dairy cows fed supplements in the milking parlour. Previous reviews focused primarily on research undertaken in situations where cows were offered ad libitum forage, whereas we consider the likely benefits of individualized supplementary feeding strategies under rotational grazing management, wherein pasture is often restricted to all or part of a herd. The review provides compelling evidence that between-cow differences in response to concentrate supplements support the concept of individualized supplementary feeding.

Introduction

In temperate regions of the world, pastures are generally the most cost-effective sources of nutrients for dairy production (Peyraud and Delaby, 2001) For example, Dillon *et al.*, (2005) highlighted that the cost of production in countries using predominantly pasture-based systems are much lower than in countries with more intensive milk production systems. Also, there is a strong positive relationship between estimates of pasture consumed per ha and farm profitability (Dairy NZ 2012; Department of Primary Industries 2012). However, efficient utilisation of pastures may be limited by a number of factors including seasonal variation in pasture availability and nutritive value (Chapman *et al.*, 2008, 2009; Roche *et al.*, 2009b,c). This is particularly so in southern Australia and the Waikato region of New Zealand where the pasture growth pattern is characterized by rapid growth of high quality pasture in Spring followed by low and variable growth of poorer quality pasture in late Summer through Winter (Chapman *et al.*, 2009; Jacobs 2014). Consequently, pasture growth and composition are highly variable (Chapman *et al.*, 2009; Roche *et al.*, 2009a,b) resulting in times of both deficit and surplus of nutrients (Hill *et al.*, 2014; Jacobs 2014). Farmers attempt to manage these fluctuations in pasture supply by seasonal (generally Spring) calving, conserving forage during periods of excess, and supplementary feeding of fodder and concentrates during deficits.

Even when there are no restrictions in the quantity and nutritive characteristics of pasture available, pasture dry matter intake (DMI) is considered the primary factor limiting milk yield (Leaver, 1985; Kolver and Muller, 1998; Bargo *et al.*, 2002; Kolver and de Veth, 2002; Dillon, 2006), particularly for cows with high genetic potential for milk production (Buckley *et al.*, 2000a,b; Horan *et al.*, 2006; Peyraud and Delagarde, 2013). To fully utilise the genetic potential of high producing dairy cows requires the consumption of more than 25 kg of DM per day which, if derived entirely from pasture, can be more than 125 kg fresh matter. This is virtually impossible to achieve under practical grazing conditions. The relationship between pasture DMI and pasture allowance is quadratic in nature, with the marginal response in DMI diminishing as pasture allowance increases (Baudrucco *et al.*, 2010). Therefore, even with the most generous (and impractical) pasture allowance, maximum DMI from pasture alone can rarely approach 20 kg DMI (Jacobs 2014). Given that maintenance requirements become an increasing proportion of total nutrient intake as DMI decreases, there is an even greater proportional reduction in milk yield when DMI is constrained. Therefore, concentrate supplements are used in pasture-based systems as a management tool either to manage deficits in pasture supply (Holmes and Roche, 2007) or to increase overall DMI and milk production (Stockdale, 2000; Bargo *et al.*, 2003).

In housed systems with cows fed a total mixed ration (TMR) a target DMI of 25 kg per day is much more achievable (Bargo *et al.*, 2002). Furthermore, it is much easier to manipulate the amount or composition of the TMR to meet the nutrient requirements of an individual or small or large group of cows with similar requirements in a housed system. Other intensive livestock industries, such as the pig and poultry industries, utilise knowledge of specific nutrient requirements in different physiological states and in some cases manipulate what is essentially a variable TMR on almost a daily basis. However, given the highly variable feed-base, which can change even within a day, it is extremely difficult to do this in grazing dairy cows on even a seasonal basis. The advent of modern feed- and milk monitoring technology that provides pivotal information of individual dairy cows combined with improvements in estimation of pasture allowance and nutrient content in virtually real time offer the potential to better match feeding strategies to individual cows (Hills *et al.*, 2015a,b). As the reliability of the information form these technologies improves, so too does the ability to target feed individual cows.

The reasons why a farmer would want to supplementary feed an individual dairy cow are numerous and include feeding to milk and component yield, body weight, body condition score, genetic potential, changes in pasture DM and composition, grazing behaviour and substitution rate, animal health and reproductive performance. A recent comprehensive review covered these reasons in depth and attempted to capture the limitations and potential of individualised supplementary feeding strategies for grazing dairy cows and readers are referred to this (Hills *et al.*, 2015a) and other reviews of supplementary feeding in pasture based systems (Bargo *et al.*, 2003; Doyle *et al.*, 2005; Baudrucco *et al.*, 2010; Wales *et al.*, 2013; Hills *et al.*, 2015a; Jacobs, 2014) for full literature coverage. The purpose of this chapter is to capture succinctly some of the most pertinent information from Hills *et al.*, (2015a) with a particular focus on likely opportunities for individualized supplementary feeding strategies under rotational grazing management, where pasture is often restricted to all or part of a herd. In doing so, it will be taken as a given that DMI (encompassing metabolisable energy (ME) but also including other nutrients) is the major nutritional limit to production in the grazing dairy cow while understanding that the nutrient profile of the consumed and digested feed can also be a limit.

Nutritional limitations of dairy cows grazing temperate pastures

Although intensively grazed forages can be of high quality, the large difference in milk yields between grazing cows and those fed a TMR is often considered proof that a nutritional deficiency in pasture limits milk production. Kolver and Muller (1998) compared cows grazing high-quality pastures (Dactylus glomerata) with cows being fed TMR and found that grazing cows consumed 19% less feed (19.0 vs 23.4 kg DMI/d) but produced 33% less milk (29.6 vs 44.1 kg/d). Simulation using the Cornell Net Carbohydrate and Protein System (Fox *et al.*, 1995) indicated that 61% of the reduced milk yield in the cows grazing pasture was due to a lower DMI, 24% of the difference was due to energy expenditure in grazing and walking, 12% was estimated to be due to excretion of surplus nitrogen, 7% reflected the greater energy content of milk from grazing cows and 5% was due to differences in partitioning of energy between milk production and body tissue. Kolver and Muller (1998) concluded that intake of nutrients, rather than a limitation in any one nutrient in pasture, was the primary factor constraining milk production from high-quality pasture, with the remaining factors reflecting differences in energy partitioning to activity, milk composition, or urea synthesis. These data confirmed the high nutritional value of temperate pastures as feeds for ruminants and emphasized that the majority of the difference in milk production between TMR-fed cows and cows grazing high-quality pasture related to the farming system and not necessarily the nutritional profile of the feed. Since DMI explained more than 60% of the difference in milk production between TMR-fed and grazing dairy cows, providing cows with a nutritionally balanced supplement should increase production through increased intake of nutrients. Indeed, concentrate supplement use in Australia increased from 0.7 to 1.7 t/cow over the 20 year period from 1990 (Dharma *et al.*, 2012).

An issue with successful use of concentrate supplements in pasture-based systems is the variability in the milk response to these supplements (Leaver, 1985; Peyraud and Delaby, 2001; Bargo *et al.*, 2003; Kellaway and Harrington, 2004; Holmes and Roche, 2007; Baudracco *et al.*, 2010), with substitution of supplementary feed for pasture having the greatest influence on the milk production response (Stockdale, 2000b; Bargo *et al.*, 2003). In general, the higher the rate of substitution of supplementary feed for pasture, the lower the average milk response to the supplement (Stockdale, 2000). If individualized feeding is to offer any advantage over flat-rate feeding then the variability in response to concentrates is what needs to be understood and exploited (Andre *et al.*, 2010a,b).

Major factors that contribute to substitution of supplements for pasture have been defined at the herd level, and include pasture availability and nutritive characteristics, cow genotype, stage of lactation, and type and nutritive characteristics of the supplement (Stockdale, 2000; Linnane *et al.*, 2004; Holmes and Roche, 2007; Roche *et al.*, 2007; Baudracco *et al.*, 2010a; Sheahan *et al.*, 2011). However, the degree to which pasture DMI varies in response to supplements at an individual animal level and the extent to which this can be exploited to improve efficiency of production is not well understood. Forage and concentrate supplementation in pasture-based systems is usually determined by the average nutritional requirements of the herd, rather than by those of individual cows. Interestingly, although dairy farmers can be responsive to a variable pasture mass and will alter the feeding rate of conserved fodder, they are much less responsive with concentrates and generally feed a flat rate of concentrates regardless of season, stage of lactation or season of calving (Walker et al., 2007).

Although ME intake is the primary nutritional factor limiting milk production in the grazing dairy cow, with increased provision of nutritionally incomplete supplements there comes a point at which other factors limit milk production. For example, total supply of amino acids or supply of individual amino acids at the small intestine can become most limiting when a low-protein cereal grain is the primary supplement, a principle well recognised in monogastric nutrition. Although microbial protein reaching the small intestine is generally of high biological value, the amino acid profile doesn't exactly reflect that of milk protein (Davis et al., 1994; Tagari et al., 1995) and may be limiting for some amino acids (e.g. lysine and leucine) and in excess for others (e.g. arginine). Furthermore, grain based supplements, particularly those based on rapidly fermentable grains such as wheat, can disrupt rumen function and reduce DMI and digestive efficiency when provided in excess (Bramley et al., 2008; Leddin et al., 2009;2010). A partial mixed ration (PMR) with the suitable balance of grain and protein supplements with suitable fermentative and digestive characteristics should ameliorate these imbalances. The challenge of course is determining, and then delivering, this "suitable" amount and profile of nutrients to an individual cow where the DMI of a changing feed base is unknown.

There is some evidence that it is possible to ameliorate some potential imbalances through provision of a balanced PMR. For example, Auldist et al., (2014) offered increasing levels of cereal grain based supplements as a PMR to grazing dairy cows in early lactation. At the highest concentrate inclusion rates (>12 kg/day) rates there was substantially less milk produced than predicted, probably as a result of associative effects of high levels of rapidly fermentable starch on fermentative capacity of NDF (Leddin et al., 2009;2010) and indicative of digestive upset. However, by replacing some of the rapidly fermented wheat with canola meal, an ingredient providing ME from fermentable NDF and CP primarily, the rumen pH and other indicators of fermentation returned to normal, and DMI and milk production increased significantly over that of the predominantly grain based PMR. Data such as these provide encouragement that it may be possible to individually supplement dairy cows with a suitable supplement provided intake and quality of pasture is known. Feeding supplements as a PMR is becoming more common in Australia, with approximately 16% of Australian dairy farmers using this system for at least part of the year (Dairy Australia 2012). Why then don't dairy farmers individually feed grazing dairy cows? The answer is complex, but is largely related to lack of knowledge about what the cows are eating at pasture and the variable responses to concentrates.

Supplementation strategies

Supplementary feeding strategies vary from flat-rate feeding, where the same amount of supplement is offered to each cow in a herd for every day of the supplementary feeding period, to more complex feeding systems in which cows are offered different amounts of supplements based on one or more parameters such as current or expected milk and milk component yield, body weight, body condition score, genetic potential, changes in pasture DM and composition, grazing behaviour and substitution rate, animal health and reproductive performance. The theoretical potential for individualized feeding of dairy cows has long been recognised and research investigating the merits of different systems has continued since the 1940s. Within a flat-rate system, concentrates can either be allocated at a constant rate throughout the lactation (the uniform flat-rate system) or be stepped up or down (stepped flat-rate) in response to stage of lactation (Leaver, 1988). A further level of complexity is introduced when a combination of ingredients and nutrient sources are used, with the objective of complementing nutrients obtained from pasture or conserved forage to optimize nutrient intake and increase milk production.

Flat- and stepped- rate feeding of concentrates

An obvious parameter to focus attention on for individualised feeding is stage of lactation and many studies have investigated whether early lactation cows would benefit more from higher rates of supplements than those in mid and late lactation rather than feeding the amount each day. In a comprehensive Danish research program investigating a range of different concentrate feeding strategies provided to cows fed grass silage ad libitum, (Ostergaard, 1979) found that although average milk yield increased in response to increasing level of concentrates offered (1,200, 1,530, or 1,850 kg of concentrate mix/ cow per lactation) there was no difference in milk yield if more concentrates were offered in early compared to later lactation (Table 1). Similarly, Gordon (1982) reported no benefit from stepped feeding over a 2-yr period, with concentrate DMI of 1,200 and 1,150 kg/cow per lactation and cows producing 4,900 and 4,850 kg/cow per lactation, with no difference in milk fat or protein yields. In that study, the grass silage offered had a relatively high ME (680 g/kg of digestible OM in DM). Taylor and Leaver (1984) hypothesized that there may be an interaction between silage quality and feeding strategy and therefore compared both flat-rate and stepped feeding allocation strategies when cows were consuming high or low ME silage (10.5 and 8.9 MJ of ME/kg of DM). Although there was no clear effect of feeding allocation method, milk yield was higher in cows fed the high ME grass silage. Similarly, Rakes and Davenport (1971) found no difference in milk yield over 3 lactations in cows fed approximately 3,250 kg of concentrate per year equal regardless of whether they were fed a constant amount or whether they were step fed relative to stage of lactation. Other studies confirm these findings (Gordon, 1982; Poole, 1987; Rijpkema et al., 1990; Aston et al., 1995).

Table 1. Total feed input and milk output/cow per year for different strategies of feeding mixed concentrate to dairy cows (adapted from Østergaard, 1979)

Strategy of feeding	L_0	$L_{-0.5}$	M_0	$M_{-0.5}$	$M_{+2,-1}$	M_{-1}	H_0	$H_{+1,-0.5}$	Standard
Grain mix kg DM	1161	1234	1585	1537	1491	1517	1841	1860	1441
Grass silage kg DM	2246	2312	2110	2072	2219	2117	2045	2022	1870
Milk fat kg	5657	5734	6062	5906	5899	5830	6388	6406	5772

L = 4.5 kg concentrate mix/cow per day
M = 6.0 kg concentrate mix/cow per day
H = 7.5 kg concentrate mix/cow per day
0 = flat rate feeding over entire lactation at either L, M or H
-0.5 = concentrate is reduced by 0.5 kg every 14 days throughout lactation
+2,-1 = concentrate is increased by 2 kg/cow every 14 days until week 12 and reduced by 1.0 kg every 14 days throughout remaining lactation
-1 = concentrate is reduced by 1.0 kg/cow every 14 days throughout lactation
+1,-0.5 = concentrate is increased by 1 kg/cow every 14 days until week 12 and reduced by 0.5 kg every 14 days throughout remaining lactation
Standard = feeding amount of concentrate based on milk yield (4.8 MJ ME/kg fat corrected milk)

Moisey and Leaver (1985) compared flat-rate feeding of mixed concentrates with a feeding strategy based on individual cow milk yield at 2 wk postcalving and reported no difference in milk yield during the first 20 wk of lactation. In a study where cows were offered 2 amounts of mixed concentrates (7 and 11 kg of concentrates per day) at either a flat or variable rate (based on individual milk yield at 2 wk postcalving) there was no significant difference in milk yield although milk fat yield was higher on the flat-rate (Taylor and Leaver, 1984). Similarly, in 4 separate studies Rijpkema *et al.*, (1990) was unable to detect any difference in milk yield between cows fed either a flat rate or according to milk production in cows fed ad libitum forage. Other studies confirm these findings (Gordon, 1982; Poole, 1987; Rijpkema *et al.*, 1990; Aston *et al.*, 1995).

Therefore, there appears to be no strong evidence that the system of concentrate allocation throughout lactation has any effect on milk production when the same total amount of concentrate is consumed and when forage is not limiting. However, the conditions under which these studies were conducted do not reflect on-farm recommended pasture allocation practices used in most rotational grazing systems.

Limitations of Previous Research

Although the robustness of the research reported above is unquestioned, an important factor must be considered in interpreting the appropriateness of the results for current grazing systems. In virtually all of the studies reviewed, the feeding strategy was investigated in either cows fed silage indoors or in cows offered unlimited forage and not under conditions where pasture allowance was limiting. Pasture allowance is considered to be the factor that has greatest effect on pasture DMI and substitution rate in a rotational grazing system (Stockdale 2000), although of course the quality of pasture available may contribute to differences. The relationship between pasture DMI and pasture allowance is quadratic in nature, with the marginal response in DMI diminishing as pasture allowance increases (Baudrucco *et al.*, 2010). This relationship predicts that maximum DMI occurs at a pasture allowance of 31 kg of DM/cow per day but such an allowance would lead to substantial wastage of pasture. Therefore, the pasture allowance of grazing dairy cows is generally restricted, with supplemental forage or concentrates being used to bridge deficits (Holmes and Roche, 2007). Furthermore, when pasture allowance is restricted, substitution of supplements for pasture is reduced and the marginal milk production response to supplements is increased and more predictable (Grainger and Mathews, 1989; Wales *et al.*, 1999; Stockdale, 2000). However, an unintended consequence of a restricted pasture allowance is increased competition between cows for pasture, which could lead to variations in the relative deficit between nutrient supply and demand for individual cows within a herd. For example, submissive cows, or those with low foraging ability, may be limited in their ability to select the highest quality pasture, which will probably reduce their milk production regardless of their genetic potential. In theory, these submissive cows should benefit by being individually provided additional concentrates. Independent of social hierarchy, it is also highly likely that cows of higher genetic potential for milk production will have greater nutrient deficits compared with cows of lower genetic merit (Penno *et al.*, 2001).

In a situation of restricted pasture allowance and supplementation, identifying those cows that have the greatest relative nutrient deficit and supplying them with more supplement than cows with smaller nutrient deficits may improve the efficiency of milk production, through low substitution of supplements for pasture in low-genetic-merit cows and more efficient partitioning of nutrients to milk in high-genetic-merit cows (Garcia *et al.*, 2007). This implies that there could be a benefit from individualized feeding in the milking parlour when pasture allowance is restricted. Garcia *et al.*, (2000) reported that when cows were fed corn silage on a restricted basis for 2 h after milking, variation in individual DMI was not associated with their milk yield but with their social hierarchy. An issue related to this social effect is the effect of the time that individual cows arrive at the pasture after milking, with those arriving last faced with increased pasture restriction and reduced pasture quality compared with those cows arriving first (Kaur *et al.*, 2013). For example, cows that arrived first to a paddock of kikuyu pasture has access to feed that had over 20% higher protein and 15% lower acid detergent fibre than those arriving last (Scott *et al.*, 2014). Similarly, if a cow spends more time in the dairy because it has been selected to be fed additional supplemental concentrates, it may arrive back at the pasture when the better quality pasture has been consumed. As a consequence the benefits of additional supplemental feed may be lost and conversely those cows that received less supplements would benefit by having access to more and better quality pasture. More research needs to be conducted to examine the social factors affecting grazing behaviour and the subsequent DMI of individual cows at pasture to determine how important these factors are in optimizing efficiency of milk production when supplementing cows in pasture-based systems. Computerized drafting systems combined with improved ability to individually feed cows will aid in this.

The only recent data exploring this question (Garcia *et al.*, 2007) compared feeding of concentrates based on individual cow milk yield (ranging from 3 to 7 kg of DM per day) with feeding a flat 5 kg of DM/cow per day, when grazing a limited allowance of lucerne and supplemented with maize silage as a forage source. Garcia *et al.*, (2007) reported a 7% increase in yield of milk fat and protein in cows fed individual allowances of concentrates relative to their milk yield, although this may in part be explained by maize silage filling the forage gap. Importantly, there was significant between-cow variation in DMI, highlighting the potential for exploiting this variability through individualized feeding strategies.

Factors affecting the response to supplements

Compelling evidence indicates that cow-level factors could be used to define appropriate individualized feeding strategies for grazing dairy cows. The dairy cow herself affects the marginal milk production and body condition score (BCS) responses to concentrate supplementation, and this effect relates, in some way, to the balance between the supply of and demand for nutritional factors (e.g., ME, protein, AA). There are cow genetic differences in concentrations of humoral hunger and satiety agents, substitution rate and total DMI, and in partitioning of nutrients between milk and BCS. With higher levels of supplementation, there is an increasing chance of different nutrient deficiencies limiting responses to supplement, such that provision of multiple feeds will be required to maximize productivity from supplementary feeding. In addition, the marginally deficient rotational grazing management protocol and aspects of behavioural hierarchy that result in greater access to pasture for some cows (e.g., whether cows are milked early or late in the milking schedule) result in a competitive environment of feed acquisition. Some combination of these cow factors, complex nutritional deficiencies, and cow × grazing management interacting factors could possibly be used to define appropriate supplementation of cows such that the final milk production response to supplementary feeds (i.e., immediate and deferred responses) will be greater than if all cows in the herd were fed similarly (i.e., flat-rate feeding). These cow-level factors will be briefly discussed below.

Grazing behaviour and substitution rate

If individualized feeding is to offer any advantage over flat rate feeding in grazing dairy systems, it is essential to understand the cow characteristics by which cows should be individually fed. In particular, those factors that affect substitution rate need to be elucidated as cows with the lowest propensity to substitute concentrate for pasture are most likely those to benefit most from individualised feeding. To this end, Stockdale (2000) reviewed the literature on substitution rate and concluded that the factors that explained the greatest amount of variation (albeit 50% remained unexplained) were pasture DMI when cows were not supplemented and the cow herself, such that substitution rate increased with increasing pasture DMI and declined with increasing cow body weight (BW). However, recent research results indicate there are also effects of cow genetics on substitution rate that are not accounted for by BW or pasture DMI (Fulkerson et al., 2008).

Linnane et al., (2004) and Sheahan et al., (2011) investigated the effect of differing genetic strains of Holstein-Friesian on grazing behaviour, DMI, and substitution rate under different supplementary feeding strategies. These studies indicated a strong effect of genetic background on substitution rate with cows selected for high production rate having a lower rate of substitution than the New Zealand Holstein-Friesian cows that were selected on the basis of a multi-variable genetic index. This is despite the New Zealand strain spending more time grazing than the other genotypes. If those cows within a herd that have low substitution rate and thus high marginal responses to supplementary feeds (Fulkerson et al., 2008) can be identified, they could be targets for individual feeding.

Although grazing dairy cows reduce the time spent grazing by approximately 12 min for every 1 kg DM of supplemental concentrate (Bargo et al., 2002;2003; Sheahan et al., 2011), this effect of supplement on grazing time isn't uniform throughout the day. The effect is only evident in the morning (Sheahan et al., 2011; 2013), indicating involvement of complex neuronal and physiological mechanisms regulating feeding in grazing dairy cows. Grazing time is not the same as pasture intake, however, as evidenced by the divergence between grazing time and substitution rate in the genetic studies mentioned above (Linnane et al., 2004; Sheahan et al., 2011). The other behavioural factors that contribute to pasture DMI are bite mass and bite rate which, along with grazing time, are behavioural proxies for the balance between the physiological factors regulating hunger and satiety and reflect a reduction in the "drive to eat" in cows provided with supplementary feed. The length of time that a cow or the herd remain on a paddock can also influence grazing behaviour. In this context, the proportion of time spent grazing decreases with increasing time spent on a paddock (Chilibroste et al., 2015) and therefore, grazing behaviour may be different in cows milked three times per day and rotated through three farmlets, as happens in many rotational grazing systems that utilise automatic milking systems.

Dry matter intake

Intake regulation is complex and has been reviewed extensively for ruminant farm animal species by Roche et al., (2008) and much of this and more recent findings for dairy cows have been captured within Hills *et al.*, (2015a). It is beyond the scope of this chapter to do credit to this complex area here and the reader is directed to these reviews and the cited primary literature for the current knowledge. Suffice to say, that neuroendocrine factors play a significant role in regulating the pasture DMI response to supplementary feeds and may, in fact, be the animal factors that contribute to the unexplained variation in substitution rate in grazing dairy cows. There is no doubt that there is also a complex interaction between these endocrine factors and body composition or condition score. Further research is required on the role of these neuroendocrine factors on DMI regulation and in the control of substitution rate. If they are suitable biomarkers for the animal effect on substitution rate, they could be used to individually feed supplements to minimize substitution rate and maximize the milk production response to supplements and, ultimately, could be used to select cows that produce more milk from every kilogram of supplement consumed, thereby enhancing feed conversion efficiency in grazing systems.

Cow genetics

Kolver *et al.*, (2002) and Kennedy *et al.*, (2003) reported genotype × diet interactions for milk production with North American Holstein-Friesian cows producing more milk when fed high-concentrate diets, either in addition to fresh pasture (Kennedy *et al.*, 2003) or in a TMR (Kolver *et al.*, 2002). Fulkerson *et al.*, (2008) expanded on this, noting that Australian Holstein-Friesian cows did not achieve the difference in milk production predicted by their estimated breeding value (EBV) when fed fresh pasture and low levels of concentrate supplements (0.3 t of DM/cow per lactation). However, when they were offered more than 0.8 t of DM supplement/cow per lactation they were able to express more of their genetic potential. These data indicate a need to consider the genetic merit of the cow when deciding on the most effective use of supplements and mean that targeting supplement based on EBV for milk fat and protein yields could allow for greater marginal milk production responses to supplementary feed. Systems of allocating concentrate based on the current milk production of the cow may not have the same effect as that reported for EBV for milk component yield. Although Bargo *et al.*, (2003) reported differences in the response to concentrate supplement between different milk yield categories, this only occurred when concentrate supplementation was greater than approximately 6 kg of DM/d, at which point the marginal response declined in low-yielding cows. Below this point, the slopes of the response lines were similar in high- and low-yielding cows. This may explain why results from previous studies indicated no benefit to individualized feeding of cows based on milk yield compared with feeding all cows the same amount of concentrate. The interactions of this cow effect with grazing management, supplement type, and supplement amount have not been adequately explored. Nonetheless, there appears to be a potential benefit to individually feeding cows concentrate feeds based on some measure of genetic merit, but the benefit probably depends on factors associated with grazing management and type of concentrate supplement.

Supplement type

Supplement type can affect the milk production response to supplements, as indicated by Auldist *et al.*, (2014). In addition to effects on milk yield, the type of supplement can also affect composition of milk, which in many parts of the world can have a profound impact on price received for milk. For example, Roche *et al.*, (2010) reported a 0.26 kg increase in milk volume per kg of DM starch-based supplement consumed when ME intake was held constant, despite no difference in energy corrected milk yield. Higgs *et al.*, (2013) confirmed this effect of starch with a 50% greater milk volume response from a maize-based concentrate than one based on fermentable fibre despite similar yields of milk solids. This effect of carbohydrate type is probably a result of differences in the output of rumen fermentation and associated differences in gluconeogenesis and glucose production. Starch-containing concentrates are primarily fermented to propionate in the rumen, which is efficiently used as a glucose precursor by the liver (Steinhour and Bauman, 1988). As glucose uptake by the mammary gland is not insulin dependent, increased hepatic glucose production should almost certainly increase production of lactose by the mammary gland and, because of the need to keep milk and blood isotonic, an increase in water movement into the secretory cells and greater milk volume.

Concentrate supplements high in starch almost always increase milk protein concentration as well as milk protein yield (Sporndly, 1991; Bargo *et al.*, 2003), provided the availability of MP is not limiting production (Mackle *et al.*, 2000). This is not an effect of ME intake, with Roche *et al.*, (2010) reporting a greater protein to fat ratio with increased starch content, although ME intake and energy-corrected milk yield did not differ. This effect of starch is almost invariably linked to the ruminal production of propionate and the associated increase in circulating insulin. In support of this, Rius *et al.*, (2010) found that abomasal infusions of starch increased plasma insulin concentrations, milk and milk protein yields, mammary plasma flow, mammary clearance rates and net mammary uptake of some amino acids. Fermentable fibre based concentrates and concentrates with high fat contents do not increase milk protein concentration and, in many instances, may reduce it indicating a failure to change the insulin–glucose axis toward increased amino acid uptake. On the other hand, Palmquist and Moser (1981) were able to reduce blood glucose and insulin concentrations and induced insulin resistance when feeding bypass fat and this could be the mechanism by which dietary fat reduces milk protein content.

The effect of concentrate supplementation on milk fat content varies with concentrate composition. Generally, fermentable fibre-based concentrates increase milk fat content and yield compared with starch-based concentrates (Higgs *et al.*, 2013), which tend to decrease milk fat content because of the increase in milk volume with no change in total fat yield (Jenkins and McGuire, 2006). However, in unusual circumstances, starch based concentrates can lead to a depression in milk fat yield. In TMR-based systems, this depression in milk fat has been attributed to production of particular isomers of conjugated linoleic acid (CLA) during ruminal biohydrogenation of linoleic acid, most notably trans-10,cis-12 CLA. However, In pasture-based systems, this particular CLA isomer is found at low concentrations in milk and is not related to milk fat content (Dunshea *et al.*, 2008) possibly because it is not an intermediary in biohydrogenation of linolenic acid (C18:3), the predominant fatty acid in pasture.

In summary, supplementation of concentrate to grazing dairy cows increases milk and milk component yield. However, the size of this response is dependent on substitution rate, and the relative proportions of fat, protein, and lactose in the increase in milk component yield is primarily dependent on supplement composition. Starch based concentrates generally increase milk protein content and yield whereas fermentable fibre based concentrates tend to lower milk protein content but increase milk protein yield through increased milk volume. Supplementation with bypass fat can lower milk protein yield. Compared with milk protein content, milk fat content is often reduced by starch based concentrates and enhanced by inclusion of fermentable fibre based concentrates.

Energy balance and body composition

A cow's body composition, as indicated by BCS, at calving and during the reproductive period, as well as the change in body composition between calving and breeding, are important parameters for milk production, health and welfare, and reproductive function (Roche *et al.*, 2009a). The importance of BCS (i.e., energy state) and energy balance at key times in the lactation cycle was extensively reviewed by Roche *et al.*, (2009a). However, given the likely effect of genetics and nutrition on body composition and change in BCS (Roche *et al.*, 2006; McCarthy *et al.*, 2007) and the effect of cow body composition on response to concentrate supplements (Stockdale, 2000a), the role of BCS in cow productivity, health, and reproduction will be discussed briefly, particularly in the context of response to concentrates.

Although labile body tissue mobilization is a natural mammalian adaptation, intensive selection for milk production has resulted in cows that are prepared to mobilize body tissue to the detriment of health and reproduction. Approximately 30 days after calving, the balance between fat mobilization and synthesis can favour fat deposition in grazing dairy cows by increasing consumption of concentrate supplements.

However, high genetic merit cows require a greater amount of concentrates to effect change in these metabolic pathways. The ability to individually offer cows concentrate supplements based on BCS or BW criteria offers a potential opportunity to improve production, reproduction, and, perhaps, health, and to enhance public perception of dairying through effective management of otherwise thin cows. In addition, the net efficiency of producing milk from BCS in grazing cows is low because of the low efficiency of BCS gain from autumn pasture (Mandok *et al.*, 2013). The efficiency of gaining condition is also 10% greater in lactating cows than in dry cows (Moe and Tyrrell, 1972; Yan *et al.*, 1997). These factors mean that the opportunity to manage BCS through individualized feeding at key periods during lactation and gestation should improve feed conversion efficiency on grazing dairy farms.

Enabling technology

A recent survey on Australian dairy-farm technology and management practices reported that 15% of Australian dairy farms had computerised bail feeding systems (Dharma *et al.*, 2012). Similar statistics exist for New Zealand (Edwards *et al.*, 2015) indicating that there is considerable opportunity for dairy farmers operating rotational grazing systems to implement differential feeding of individual cows. However, as outlined previously, a major impediment to individualized feeding is the ability to measure the amount and quality of pasture consumed by each individual cow. Only then, can a farmer feed an individual cow to either milk and milk component yield, BW, BCS, genetic potential, changes in pasture DM and composition, grazing behaviour and substitution rate, animal health or reproductive performance that they desire. Fortunately, technology is becoming available that can assist in providing this information (Greenwood *et al.*, 2014; Hills *et al.*, 2015b).

Hand held pasture meters such as rising plate meters have been available for many years to measure pasture availability in either a research or a commercial setting. More recently, electronic pasture meters, such as the C-Dax pasture meter, that can be attached to a motorbike have been developed to provide rapid assessment of pasture mass (Rennie *et al.*, 2009; Oudshoorn *et al.*, 2011). Interestingly, some data generated with an electronic pasture meter identified considerable variation in pasture height even within a plot (see Hills *et al.*, 2015b) highlighting the high inter- and intra-paddock variability in pasture available (Laca 2009) and the complexity in pasture nutrient availability, let alone intake. There has been considerable development in the horticultural industries where imaging coupled with use of drones has been used to assess canopy cover and water stress (Fuentes *et al.*, 2013). Another issue is that pasture composition can vary during the day and it would be useful to be able to monitor some of these changes. In this context, Watanabe *et al.*, (2014) reported that they could determine pasture biomass crude protein with reasonable accuracy with a handheld near infrared reflectometer

(NIR), although forage biomass was predicted with less precision. Although promising, these technologies still need further development if they are to be implemented on farm. Of course, pasture availability and composition are only part of what is required to estimate nutrient intake from pasture and real time measurement of individual pasture intake still remains the holy-grail in extensive systems.

Development of electronic sensing capability has the potential to allow measurement of traits of economic importance that previously had not been measurable in the commercial grazing environment (Greenwood *et al.*, 2014). In particular, where an animal grazes in a paddock if linked with estimates of pasture growth and composition can provide more accurate estimates of individual cow intake. If further coupled with feeding behaviour measures it may be possible to make even better predictions of DM and nutrient intake from pasture. For example, Woodward (1997) showed that the DMI of grazing cows could be estimated from a time budget of searching, prehension, mastication and rumination in grazing animals. Furthermore, the number of bites, grazing and ruminating time, and daily intake can be derived as functions of bite mass and composition (Gibb *et al.*, 1997). There are now commercially available halter technologies compatible with many automatic or retro-fitted traditional milking systems that provide estimates of bite and rumination characteristics. Furthermore, ear tag sensors with extended battery life and miniaturised specialised sensors and accelerometers are continuously being developed (Greenwood *et al.*, 2014).

The ability to stack these technologies along with real time information derived from computerised milking systems and the ability to individually feed and draft within or around the milking shed will ultimately allow farmers to individually feed concentrates to dairy cows grazing in rotational grazing systems. A challenge will be the ability to handle the complexity of information and not be a slave to the data (Hills *et al.*, 2015b). Perhaps the use of models, especially those with the ability to "learn" or "train" can assist in utilising much of this data (Romera *et al.*, 2010; Gregorini *et al.*, 2015).

Conclusions and recommendations

The existence of variability between animals is critical in achieving potential benefits from individualized management strategies, such as supplementary feeding. Variability between animals in their response to concentrate supplements provides an opportunity to optimize the use of feed supplements at an individual cow level. Although much of the past research conducted under conditions of ad libitum feeding failed to identify any advantage to individualized feeding strategies, there is a need to determine responses to individualized feeding strategies in rotational grazing situations, in which pasture allowance is restricted. This chapter highlights the complexity in determining responses to supplementary feeds and has provided compelling evidence that both cow-level (e.g., genotype, parity, DIM, BW, BCS, DMI) and system-level (e.g., pasture allowance and other grazing management strategies and climate) parameters can influence marginal milk production response to supplements. The challenge remains to identify parameters or combination of parameters that may enable improvement in marginal milk production response to supplements as a result of a reallocation of supplements according to individual cow requirements rather than at the same flat rate to all animals in the herd. The significant gaps in our understanding of the consequences of individualized feeding in a restricted pasture-based grazing system highlight the need to develop an integrated research program that analyses the potential of parameters discussed in this review, under more controlled research conditions and under differing systems. Of particular priority in pasture-based systems is research to quantify variation in DMI between animals and the nutritive content of pasture consumed. Although pasture DMI and nutritive content cannot currently be measured routinely, these two factors have the potential to significantly affect both milk and BCS responses to concentrate supplements. There is also a need for longer-term comparisons of flat-rate feeding with individualized feeding in restricted pasture-based dairy systems. Research should be designed to allow for not only comparison of feeding systems, but also acquisition of key data that could be used to develop new algorithms, which may, in turn, improve the way supplements are fed to cows. Gaining a better understanding of the potential benefits for individualized feeding will enable assessment of the cost:benefit ratio for investing in technology for individualized feeding.

References

Andre, G., Berentsen, P.B.M., Engel, B., de Koning, C. and Lansink, A. (2010a) Increasing the revenues from automatic milking by using individual variation in milking characteristics. *Journal of Dairy Science*, **93**, 942-953.

Andre, G., Berentsen, P.B.M., Van Duinkerken, G. Engel, B., de Koning, C. and Lansink, A (2010b) Economic potential of individual variation in milk yield response to concentrate intake of dairy cows. *Journal of Agricultural Science*, **148**, 263-276.

Aston, K., Sutton, J.D. and Fisher, W.J. (1995) Milk production from grass-silage diets - Strategies for concentrate allocation. *Animal Science*, **61**, 465-480.

Auldist, M.J., Marett, L.C., Greenwood, J.S., Wright, M.M., Hannah, M., Jacobs, J.L. and Wales, W.J. (2014) Replacing wheat with canola meal in a partial mixed ration increases the milk production of cows grazing at a restricted pasture allowance in spring. *Animal Production Science*, **54**, 869–878.

Bargo, F., Muller, L.D., Delahoy, J.E. and Cassidy, T.W. (2002). Milk response to concentrate supplementation of high producing dairy cows grazing at two pasture allowances. *Journal of Dairy Science*, **85**, 1777-1792.

Bargo, F., Muller, L.D., Kolver, E.S. and Delahoy, J.E. (2003) Production and digestion of supplemented dairy cows on pasture. *Journal of Dairy Science*, **86**, 1-42.

Baudracco, J., Lopez-Villalobos, N., Holmes, C.W. and Macdonald, K.A. (2010) Effects of stocking rate, supplementation, genotype and their interactions on grazing dairy systems: a review. *New Zealand Journal of Agricultural Research*, **53**, 109-133.

Bramley, E., Lean, I.J., Fulkerson, W.J., Stevenson, M.A., Rabiee, A.R. and Costa, N.D. (2008). The definition of acidosis in dairy herds predominantly fed on pasture and concentrates. *Journal of Dairy Science*, **91**, 308-321.

Buckley, F., Dillon, P., Crosse, S., Flynn, F. and Rath, M. (2000a) The performance of Holstein Friesian dairy cows of high and medium genetic merit for milk production on grass-based feeding systems. *Livestock Production Science*, **64**, 107-119.

Buckley, F., Dillon, P., Rath, M. and Veerkamp, R.F. (2000b) The relationship between genetic merit for yield and live weight, condition score, and energy balance of spring calving Holstein Friesian dairy cows on grass based systems of milk production. *Journal of Dairy Science*, **83**, 1878-1886.

Chapman, D.F., Kenny, S.N., Beca, D. and Johnson, I.R. (2008) Pasture and forage crop systems for non-irrigated dairy farms in southern Australia. 2. Inter-annual variation in forage supply, and business risk. *Agricultural Systems*, **97**, 126-138.

Chapman, D.F., Cullen, B.R. Johnson, I.R. and Beca, D. (2009) Interannual variation in pasture growth rate in Australian and New Zealand dairy regions and its consequences for system management. *Animal Production Science*, **49**, 1071-1079.

Chilibroste, P., Gibb, M.J., Soca, P. and Mattiauda, D.A. (2015) Behavioural adaptation of grazing cows to changes in feeding management: do they follow a predictable pattern? *Animal Production Science*, **55**, 1071-1079.

Dairy NZ (2012) 'New Zealand dairy statistics.' (DairyNZ Ltd: Hamilton, New Zealand).

Davis, T.A., Nguyen, H.V., Garcia-Bravo, R., Fiorotto, M.L., Jackson, E.M., Lewis, D.G., Lee D.R. and Reeds, P.J. (1994) Amino acid composition of human milk is not unique. *Journal of Nutrition*, **124**, 1126-1132.

Department of Primary Industries (2012) 'Dairy industry farm monitor project: summary of results 11/12.' (*The State of Victoria, Department of Primary Industries: Melbourne*).

Dharma, S., Shafron, W., Oliver, M. (2012) 'Australian dairy: farm technology and management practices 2010–11.' (*Australian Bureau of Agricultural and Resource Economics and Sciences: Canberra*).

Dillon, P., Roche, J.R., Shalloo, L. and Horan, B. (2005) Optimising financial return from grazing in temperate pastures. In '*Utilisation of grazed grass in temperate animal systems. Proceedings of a satellite workshop of the XXth international grassland congress, Cork, Ireland*'. (Ed. J.J. Murphy) pp. 131–148. (Wageningen Academic Publishers: Wageningen, The Netherlands)

Dillon, P. (2006). Achieving high dry-matter intake from pasture with grazing dairy cows. Pages 1-26 in *Fresh herbage for dairy cattle: the key to a sustainable food chain*. A. Elgersma, J. Dijkstra, and S. Tamminga, ed. Springer Verlag, Heidelberg Germany.

Doyle, P.T., Francis, S.A., Stockdale, C.R. (2005) Associative effects between feeds when concentrate supplements are fed to grazing dairy cows: a review of likely impacts on metabolisable energy supply. *Australian Journal of Agricultural Research*, **56**, 1315–1329.

Dunshea, F.R, Ostrowska, E., Walker, G.P., and Doyle, P.T. (2008) Seasonal variation in the concentrations of conjugated linoleic and trans fatty acids in milk fat from commercial dairy farms is associated with pasture and grazing management and supplementary feeding practices. *Australian Journal of Experimental Agriculture*, **48**, 1062-1065.

Edwards, J.P., Dela Rue, B.T. and Jago JG (2015) Evaluating rates of technology adoption and milking practices on New Zealand dairy farms. *Animal Production Science*, **55**, 702–709

Fox, D. G., Barry, M.C., Pitt, R.E., Roseler, D.K. and Stone, W.C. (1995) Application of the Cornell net carbohydrate and protein model for cattle consuming forages. *Journal of Animal Science*, **73**, 267–277.

Fuentes, S., De Bei, R. and Yyerman, S.D. (2013) New and emerging technologies for the vineyard. The vineyard of the future initiative. *Wine and Viticulture Journal*, **28**, 38-45.

Fulkerson, W.J., Davison, T.M., Garcia, S.C., Hough, G., Goddard, M.E., Dobos, R. and Blockey, M. (2008). Holstein-Friesian dairy cows under a predominantly grazing system: Interaction between genotype and environment. *Journal of Dairy Science*, **91**, 826-839.

Garcia, S. C., Holmes, C.W., Hodgson, J. and MacDonald, A. (2000) The combination of the n-alkanes and C-13 techniques to estimate individual dry matter intakes of herbage and maize silage by grazing dairy cows. *Journal of Agricultural Science*, **135**, 47-55.

Garcia, S. C., Pedernera, M., Fulkerson, W.J., Horadagoda, A. and Nandra, K. (2007) Feeding concentrates based on individual cow requirements improves the yield of milk solids in dairy cows grazing restricted pasture. *Australian Journal of Experimental Agriculture*, **47**, 502-508.

Gibb, M.J., Huckle, C.A., Nuthall, R. and Rook, A.J. (1997) Effect of sward surface height on intake and grazing behaviour by lactating Holstein Friesian cows. *Grass and Forage Science*, **52**, 309-321.

Gordon, F. J. (1982) The effect of pattern of concentrate allocation on milk-production for autumn-calving heifers. *Animal Production*, **34**, 55-61.

Grainger, C. and Mathews, G.L. (1989) Positive relation between substitution rate and pasture allowance for cows receiving concentrates. *Australian Journal of Experimental Agriculture*, **29**, 355-360.

Greenwood, P.L., Valencia, P., Overs, L., Raull, D.R. and Purvis, I.W. (2014) New ways of measuring intake, efficiency and behaviour of grazing livestock. *Animal Production Science*, **54**, 2796-1804.

Higgs, R. J., Sheahan, A.J., Mandok, K., Van Amburgh, M.E. and Roche, J.R. (2013) The effect of starch-, fiber-, or sugar-based supplements on nitrogen utilization in grazing dairy cows. *Journal of Dairy Science*, **96**, 3857-3866.

Hill, J., Chapman, D.F., Tharmaraj, J., Jacobs, J.L. and Cullen, B. (2014) Increasing home-grown forage consumption and profit in non-irrigated dairy systems. 3. Milk production and composition, body weight and body condition score. *Animal Production Science*, **54**, 247–255.

Hills, J.L., Wales, W.J., Dunshea, F.R., Garcia, S.C. and Roche, J.R. (2015) An evaluation of the likely effects of individualized feeding of concentrate supplements to pasture-based dairy cows. *Journal of Dairy Science*, **98**, 1363-1401

Hills, J.L., Garcia, S.C., Dela Rue, BB. And Clark, C.E.F. (2015a) Limitations and potential for individualised feeding of concentrate supplements to grazing cows. *Animal Production Science*, **55**, 922-930.

Holmes, C. W. and Roche, J.R. (2007) Pastures and supplements in dairy production systems. *Occasional Address - New Zealand Society of Animal Production*, **14**, 221-242.

Horan, B., Faverdin, P., Delaby, L., Rath, M. and Dillon, P. (2006) The effect of strain of Holstein-Friesian dairy cow and pasture-based system on grass intake and milk production. *Animal Science*, **82**, 435–444.

Jacobs, J.L. (2014) Challenges in ration formulation in pasture-based milk production systems. *Animal Production Science*, **54**, 1130-1140.

Kaur, R., Clarke, C., Horadagoda, A., Golder, H., Garcia, S., Kerrisk, K. and Islam, M.D. (2013) Increasing feed conversion efficiency in automatic milking systems: The impact of grain-based concentrate allocation and kikuyu (Pennisetum clandestinum) pasture state on milk production. Pages 1723–1724 in *22nd International Grasslands Congress: Revitalising Grasslands to Sustain our Communities*. Vol. **22**, Sydney, Australia. New South Wales Department of Primary Industry, Orange, NSW, Australia.

Jenkins, T. C. and McGuire, M.A. (2006) Major advances in nutrition: Impact on milk composition. *Journal of Dairy Science*, **89**, 1302-1310.

Kellaway, R. and Harrington, T. (2004) *Feeding concentrates: supplements for dairy cows.* Landlink Press, Melbourne.

Kennedy, J., Dillon, P., Delaby, L., Faverdin, P., Stakelum, G. and Rath, M. (2003) Effect of genetic merit and concentrate supplementation on grass intake and milk production with Holstein Friesian dairy cows. *Journal of Dairy Science*, **86**, 610-621.

Kolver, E. S. and Muller, L.D. (1998) Performance and nutrient intake of high producing Holstein cows consuming pasture or a total mixed ration. *Journal of Dairy Science*, **81**, 1403-1411.

Kolver, E. S. and de Veth, M.J. (2002) Prediction of ruminal pH from pasture-based diets. *Journal of Dairy Science*, **85**, 1255-1266.

Kolver, E. S., Roche, J.R., de Veth, M.J., Thorne, P.L. and Napper, A.R. (2002) Total mixed rations versus pasture diets: evidence for a genotype*diet interaction in dairy cow performance. *Proceedings of the New Zealand Society of Animal Production*, **62**, 246-251.

Laca, E.A. (2009) New approaches and tools for grazing management. *Rangeland Ecology and Management*, **62**, 407–417.

Leaver, J.D. (1985) Milk production from grazed temperate grassland. *Journal of Dairy Research*, **52**, 313-344.

Leaver, J. D. (1988) Level and pattern of concentrate allocation to dairy cows. Pages 315-326 in *Nutrition and lactation in the dairy cow.* P.C. Garnsworthy, ed. Butterworths, London.

Leddin, C.M., Stockdale, C.R., Hill, J., Heard, J.W. and Doyle, P.T. (2009) Increasing amounts of crushed wheat fed with pasture hay reduced dietary fiber digestibility in lactating dairy cows. *Journal of Dairy Science*, **92**, 2747-2757.

Leddin, C.M., Stockdale, C.R., Hill, J., Heard, J.W. and Doyle, P.T. (2010) Increasing amounts of crushed wheat fed with Persian clover herbage reduced ruminal pH and dietary fibre digestibility in lactating dairy cows. *Animal Production Science*, **50**, 837-846.

Linnane, M., Horan, B., Connolly, J., O'Connor, P., Buckley, F. and Dillon, P. (2004) The effect of strain of Holstein-Friesian and feeding system on grazing behaviour, herbage intake and productivity in the first lactation. *Animal Science*, **78**, 169-178.

Mackle, T.R., Dwyer, D.A., Ingvartsen, K.L., Chouinard, P.Y., Ross D.A, and Bauman, D.E. (2000) Effects of insulin and postruminal supply of protein on use of amino acids by the mammary gland for milk protein synthesis. *Journal of Dairy Science*, **83**, 93-105.

Mandok, K.S., Kay, J.K., Greenwood, S.L., Edwards, G.R. and Roche, J.R. (2013) Requirements for zero energy balance of nonlactating, pregnant dairy cows fed fresh autumn pasture are greater than currently estimated. *Journal of Dairy Science*, **96**, 4070-4076.

McCarthy, S., Berry, D.P., Dillon, P., Rath, M. and Horan, B. (2007) Influence of Holstein-Friesian strain and feed system on body weight and body condition score lactation profiles. *Journal of Dairy Science*, **90**, 1859-1869.

Moe, P.W. and Tyrrell, H.F. (1972) Metabolizable energy requirements of pregnant dairy-cows. *Journal of Dairy Science*, **55**, 480-483.

Moisey, F. R. and Leaver, J.D. (1985) Systems of concentrate allocation for dairy cattle. 3. A comparison of 2 flat-rate feeding systems at 2 amounts of concentrates. *Animal Production*, **40**, 209-217.

Østergaard, V. (1979) Optimum feeding strategies during lactation. Pages 171-194 in *Feeding Strategy for the high yielding cow* W.H.Broster and H. Swan, ed. Crosby, Lockwood Staples, London.

Oudshoorn, F.W., Hansson, S.L. and Hansen, H. (2011) Calibration of the C-Dax Pasture Meter in a Danish grazing system. *Grassland Science*, **16**, 166-168.

Palmquist, D.L. and Moser, E.A. (1981) Dietary fat effects on blood insulin, glucose utilization, and milk protein content of lactating cows. *Journal of Dairy Science*, **64**, 1664-1670.

Penno, J.W., Macdonald, K.A. and Holmes, C.W. (2001) Toward a predictive model of supplementary feeding response from grazing dairy cows. *Proceedings of the New Zealand Society of Animal Production*, **61**, 229-233.

Peyraud, J.L. and Delaby, L. (2001) Ideal concentrate feeds for grazing dairy cows - responses to supplementation in interaction with grazing management and grass quality. Page 203 in *Recent Advances in Animal Nutrition*. P.C. Garnsworthy and J. Wiseman, ed. Nottingham University Press, Nottingham, UK.

Peyraud, J.L. and Delagarde, R. (2011) Managing variations in dairy cow nutrient supply under grazing. *Animal*, **7**, 57-67.

Poole, D.A. (1987) Flat v step feeding of medium or high-levels of concentrates for dairy cows. *Animal Production*, **45**, 335-344.

Rakes, A.H. and Davenport, D.G. (1971) Response of dairy cows to two systems of distributing annual concentrates over lactation cycle. *Journal of Dairy Science*, **54**, 1300.

Rennie, G.M., King, W.M., Puha, M.R., Dalley, D.E., Dynes, R.A. and Upsdell, M.P. (2009) Calibration of the C-DAX Rapid Pasture meter and the rising plate meter for kikuyu based Northland dairy pastures. *Proceedings of the New Zealand Grassland Association*, **71**, 49-55

Rijpkema, Y.S., Vanreeuwijk, L. and Goedhart, P.W. (1990) Effects of pattern of concentrate feeding on milk-production of dairy cows offered silage ad-libitum. *Netherlands Journal of Agricultural Science*, **38**, 461-474.

Rius, A.G., Appuhamy, J.A.D.R.N., Cyriac, J., Kirovski, D., Becvar, O., Escobar, J., McGilliard, M.L., Bequette, B.J., Akers, R.J. and Hanigan, M.D. (2010) Regulation of protein synthesis in mammary glands of lactating dairy cows by starch and amino acids. *Journal of Dairy Science*, **93**, 3114-3127.

Roche, J. R., Berry, D.P. and Kolver, E.S. (2006) Holstein-Friesian strain and feed effects on milk production, body weight, and body condition score profiles in grazing dairy cows. *Journal of Dairy Science*, **89**, 3532-3543.

Roche, J.R., Sheahan, A.J., Chagas, L.M. and Berry, D.P. (2007) Concentrate supplementation reduces postprandial plasma ghrelin in grazing dairy cows: A possible neuroendocrine basis for reduced pasture intake in supplemented cows. *Journal of Dairy Science*, **90**, 1354-1363.

Roche, J.R., Blache, D., Kay, J.K., Miller, D.R., Sheahan, A.J. and Miller, D.W. (2008) Neuroendocrine and physiological regulation of intake with particular reference to domesticated ruminant animals. *Nutrition Research Reviews*, **21**, 207-234.

Roche, J.R., Friggens, N.C., Kay, J.K., Fisher, M.W., Stafford, K.J. and Berry, D.P. (2009a) Invited review: Body condition score and its association with dairy cow productivity, health, and welfare. *Journal of Dairy Science*, **92**, 5769-5801.

Roche, J.R., Turner, L.R., Lee, J.M., Edmeades, D.C., Donaghy, D.J., Macdonald, K.A., Penno, J.W. and Berry, D.P. (2009b) Weather, herbage quality and milk production in pastoral systems. 2. Temporal patterns and intra-relationships in herbage quality and mineral concentration parameters. *Animal Production Science*, **49**, 200-210.

Roche, J.R., Turner, L.R., Lee, J.M., Edmeades, D.C., Donaghy, D.J., Macdonald, K.A., Penno, J.W. and Berry, D.P. (2009c) Weather, herbage quality and milk production in pastoral systems. 3. Inter-relationships and associations between weather variables and herbage growth rate, quality and mineral concentration. *Animal Production Science*, **49**, 211-221.

Roche, J. R., Kay, J.K., Phyn, C.V.C., Meier, S., Lee, J.M. and Burke, C.R. (2010) Dietary structural to nonfiber carbohydrate concentration during the transition period in grazing dairy cows. *Journal of Dairy Science*, **93**, 3671-3683.

Romera, A.J., Beukes, P., Clark, C., Clark, D., Levy, H. and Tait, A. (2010) Use of a pasture growth model to estimate herbage mass at a paddock scale and assist management on dairy farms. *Computers and Electronics in Agriculture*, **74**, 66–72

Scott, B.A., Clark, C.E.F., Camacho, A., Golder, H., Molfino, J., Kerrisk, K.L., Lean, I., García. S.C., Chaves, A.V. and Hall, E. (2014) 'The nutritive value of pasture ingested by dairycows varies within a herd, *6th Australiasian dairy science symposium*.' (Hamilton, New Zealand).

Sheahan, A.J., Kolver, E.S. and Roche, J.R. (2011) Genetic strain and diet effects on grazing behavior, pasture intake, and milk production. *Journal of Dairy Science*, **94**, 3583-3591.

Sheahan, A.J., Boston, R.C. and Roche, J.R. (2013) Diurnal patterns of grazing behavior and humoral factors in supplemented dairy cows. *Journal of Dairy Science*, **96**, 3201-3210.

Sporndly, E. (1991) Supplementation of dairy cows offered freshly cut herbage ad-libitum with starchy concentrates based on barley or fibrous concentrates based on unmolassed sugar-beet pulp and wheat bran. *Swedish Journal of Agricultural Research*, **21**, 131-139.

Steinhour, W.D. and Bauman, D.E. (1988). Propionate metabolism: A new interpretation. Pages 238-256 in *Aspects of Digestive Physiology in Ruminants*. A. Dobson and M.J. Dobson, ed. Comstock Publications, Ithaca, NY.

Stockdale, C.R. (2000a) Differences in body condition and body size affect the responses of grazing dairy cows to high-energy supplements in early lactation. *Australian Journal of Experimental Agriculture*, **40**, 903-911.

Stockdale, C.R. (2000b) Levels of pasture substitution when concentrates are fed to grazing dairy cows in northern Victoria. *Australian Journal of Experimental Agriculture*, **40**, 913-921.

Tagari, H., Arieli, A., Mabjeesh, S., Bruckental, I., Zamwell, S. and Aharoni, Y. (1995) Assessment of duodenal amino-acid profile in dairy-cows by the in-situ method. *Livestock Production Science*, **42**, 13-22.

Taylor, W. and Leaver, J.D. (1984) Systems of concentrate allocation for dairy cattle. 2. A comparison of 2 patterns of allocation for autumn-calving cows offered 2 qualities of grass-silage ad-libitum. *Animal Production*, **39**, 325-333.

Wales, W.J., Doyle, P.T., Stockdale, C.R. and Dellow, D. (1999) Effects of variations in herbage mass, allowance, and level of supplement on nutrient intake and milk production of dairy cows in spring and summer. *Australian Journal of Experimental Agriculture*, **39**, 119-130.

Wales, W.J., Marett, L.C., Greenwood, J.S., Wright, M.M., Thornhill, J.B., Jacobs, J.L., Ho, C.K.M. and Auldist, M.J. (2013) Use of partial mixed rations in pasturebased dairying in temperate regions of Australia. *Animal Production Science*, **53**, 1167–1178.

Walker, G.P., Williams, R., Doyle, P.T. and Dunshea, F.R. (2007) Seasonal variation in milk production and cheese yield from commercial dairy farms located in northern Victoria is associated with pasture and grazing management and supplementary feeding practices. *Australian Journal of Experimental Agriculture*, **47**, 509-524.

Watanabe, N., Sakanoue, S., Lee, H-J., Lim J., Yoshioshi, R. and Kawamura, K. (2014). Use of a hand-held crop growth measuring device to estimate forage crude protein mass of pasture. *Grassland Science*, **60**, 214-224.

Woodward, S.J. (1997) Formulae for predicting animal's daily intake of pasture and grazing time from bite weight and composition. *Livestock Production Science*, **52**, 1-10.

Yan, T., Gordon, F.J., Agnew, R.E., Porter, M.G. and Patterson, D.C. (1997) The metabolisable energy requirement for maintenance and the efficiency of utilisation of metabolisable energy for lactation by dairy cows offered grass silage-based diets. *Livestock Production Science*, **51**, 141-150.

3

Farm And Laboratory Assessment Of Mineral Availability In Ruminants

N. KENDALL[1] AND P. BONE[2]

[1] *University of Nottingham, School of Veterinary Medicine and Science, Sutton Bonington Campus Loughborough LE12 5RD*

[2] *Ruminant Mineral Consultancy Limited. 39 Stratton Heights, Cirencester, GL7 2RH*

Introduction

Assessment of mineral status or availability cannot be split into separate sections - farm and laboratory - as both are intrinsically linked. Farm information is required to help determine which lab tests are required to investigate which problems the stock are experiencing, then lab information will need to be interpreted with reference to the farm situation.

The approach to assessing mineral status at farm level is very much a team approach, by working in a TEAM, together everyone achieves more! The team for assessment of mineral status should include the farmer/farm manager, the farm's veterinarian, the farm's nutritional consultant and / or commercial feed advisor. It may also include sales people and an accountancy/business consultant.

When using the TEAM approach it is important to hold an initial meeting to consider the problems and set out a plan of action. The plan will include examination of diet formulation, all mineral supplements (including direct to animal supplementation, e.g. bolus/drench) and then determine what samples are required from the diet and animal to further the investigation. Inputs and supplements must be considered on a historical and current basis as some macro and micro mineral element statuses will be affected by historical inputs.

Mineral nutrition is a broad topic with at least 7 macro and 8 micro elements (Table 1) which need to be routinely considered. There is not one common approach that can simply be used to investigate all of these elements. Ruminants also have the complexity that they are rarely fed complete diets similar to those fed to the non-ruminant pig, poultry or companion animal sectors. Ruminants are usually fed diets which include a variety of variable forages and grazing, which change with crop type and season, and the added problem of soil pH, compaction and waterlogging which alter uptake of elements from the soil into the plant. An additional complication is that the soil, crop and animal all have different requirements for macro and micro elements, meaning that optimal minerals for plant growth do not usually match the animals' requirements and optimally growing plants often fail to meet animal requirements for certain elements.

Table 1. Macro and micro elements of nutritional importance (in no particular order)

Macro element	Micro element
Calcium (Ca)	Manganese (Mn)
Phosphorus (P)	Zinc (Zn)
Magnesium (Mg)	Cobalt (Co)
Potassium (K)	Copper (Cu)
Sodium (Na)	Selenium (Se)
Chloride (Cl)	Iodine (I)
Sulphur (S)	Iron (Fe)
	Molybdenum (Mo)

Often minerals are used as a magic bullet, the answer to poor performance in the flock/herd. However, largely this is not the case and before investigating a problem as a mineral issue you must first check that there is adequate dry matter intake (i.e. enough food), adequate energy and protein intakes (good enough quality food) and adequate available clean palatable water. Additionally the disease/health status of the herd / flock should be known as this can often be confounded with nutritional issues

Once we have established that we have feed, energy, protein and water availability then minerals could be an issue and we should consider a mineral audit of the farm unless there is an obvious health issue.

It is essential to determine why you are investigating mineral status. The farmer is most likely to be the instigator, although the vet should have a significant input if there are any clinical signs of mineral imbalance. The nutritional consultant might suspect problems based on performance or dietary formulations and ingredients, whilst a business consultant/accountant should notice any decrease in financial performance. A nutritional consultant or sales person could instigate investigation of mineral status to support product sales or investigation/proof of product performance.

To start the investigation there are general parameters that we need to look at on farm including:

• Health issues / status

• Production / performance e.g. conception rate, milk yield, growth rate, pregnancy scan

- Diet Formulated, offered and fed
- Water source / access
- History of supplementation / treatments

Assessment of mineral status

To fully audit mineral status of the farm we need to gather information which includes the diet, as formulated, as fed and as consumed; three things that can be surprisingly different due to inaccuracies in weighing out, changes in dietary ingredient composition, weather (has it just rained or been very hot and dry), dietary sorting by stock or mechanically on particle size, availability of feed (empty feed trough!), palatability or dry matter intake issues.

To gain the best information it is best to work with a check list. We need to check the basics including both minerals which are naturally in the feed and those that are included at point of manufacture or added or supplemented on farm.

1. Has forage and /or grazing been analysed? The biggest variable in the diet will always be grazing or conserved forage, which usually forms the major proportion of the diet and should be tested regularly for mineral content.

2. Is the information given by manufacturers on the declaration label of purchased compounded feeds a complete mineral specification, or is it the minimum legal requirement? If unsure contact the supplier and confirm the full specification.

3. Are all bagged mineral inputs fully specified, weighed out, and mixed correctly? If unsure contact the supplier and confirm the full specification. The amount of mineral purchased should also be checked against daily feed recommendations and stock numbers to check under feeding or over supplementation.

4. Have all mineral inputs been taken into account? It is vital to make sure that all mineral inputs are included in the audit. These would include mineral buckets / licks, boluses, drenches, injectables, and mineral supplied via livestock drinking water. When carrying out this audit we must cover all management of the complete livestock cycle.

5. Do all the elements match requirements? Once totals have been calculated and dry matter intake confirmed, this will identify elements which do not meet daily requirement (i.e. likely to cause deficiency) or those which are being oversupplied and could cause problems, either due to mineral interactions or mineral accumulation/loading.

6. Have you remembered to check the water? One often forgotten input is livestock drinking water; any supply that comes from a private source should be analysed

for its mineral content. This should be done for two reasons: the supply may have concentrations of iron, manganese and sulphur which will depress palatability and hence water intake, or may interact with other elements causing mineral imbalance.

The audit of the diet may determine what needs to be investigated in the animal, although animal sampling may also be driven by clinical signs, farm history or local factors (e.g. geology).

Animal blood, urine and tissue samples

When sampling animals we are only going to consider three sample types: blood, liver and urine. Personally, we have not found other animal samples to be of significant use.

Urine is a useful indicator of mineral intakes, especially for elements which are heavily regulated homeostatically (e.g. macro-minerals such as calcium) and can be corrected for dilution factors. Blood is useful for assessing current mineral status, or using enzymes and metabolites, particularly if red blood cell related, to give a longer term indication of status. Liver is useful to monitor/diagnose accumulation of elements (e.g. copper) or a long term sustained deficiency.

When sending blood, urine or liver samples they must be packed according to UN3373, packing instruction 650 (primary tube, absorbent material, secondary watertight packaging, labelled outer with UN3373 label return address and postage). When posting consider using guaranteed next day services and be mindful of how the sample is handled and kept between sampling and dispatch (a fridge is much better than rolling around the boot of a car). Samples must be clearly labelled and should be submitted with paperwork for the lab.

Blood

With blood there are many different types of tubes, with or without different anticoagulants, so it is worth checking with the laboratory prior taking the sample to make sure an appropriate quantity of the correct sample is taken.

Blood samples are best taken by a veterinarian and are usually taken by jugular venepuncture in sheep, and via the jugular or coccygeal (tail) vein in cattle. Blood samples can be collected at slaughter, but the sample tends to haemolyse more readily and certain parameters are altered for this type of sampling (Please check with lab). Blood samples usually cannot be stored frozen prior to processing as red cells lyse and the serum/plasma will be haemolysed; samples can, however, be refrigerated but it is important to get the samples to the lab in a timely manner (ideally next day). There are many different options for anticoagulants, or none if serum is required, so please check type of tubes and volumes required with the lab. In general, most mineral work is carried out on lithium heparin whole blood and plasma (often these vacutainer tubes are green topped) or serum from plain or clotting activator tubes (often these vacutainer tubes are red topped).

Liver

Liver is easier to collect post slaughter at the abattoir e.g. from cull cows, cast ewes or finishing lambs, but liver can also be collected by biopsy (veterinary procedure) in cattle (not sheep) and a good opportunistic practice is to retain a sample from any casualty slaughters as they are often the best animal in the herd! Liver for mineral determinations can usually be keep frozen, which allows batches for analysis to be collected over time, but please check with the lab first.

Urine

Urine can be collected from sheep and cattle by free catch, but in female cattle it is possible to stimulate urine by gently massaging below the vulva. When catching a stream of cow urine it is best to collect the mid flow from the top of the stream as this is less contaminated with faeces. Alternately, urine can be collected via cannulation but this is a veterinary procedure and has the risk of introducing urinary tract damage or urinary tract infections. Urine samples can be stored short term in the fridge or frozen over a longer term, but please check with the lab first.

Animal mineral status interpretation

Interpretation of animal sample results should not be done in isolation and is best done 'on farm' by someone with appropriate expertise that has seen the animals and the diets (Vet or nutritionist) or by the TEAM!

Measurement of more than one status indicator, although likely to add to the cost, will often tell you more than using either or even both singly. For example if considering selenium status we can analyse plasma selenium and erytrocyte glutathione peroxidase, plasma selenium inidcates the recent selenium intake (2-3 days), whilst glutathione peroxidase (GSHPx) as it is a red blood cell measure is relient on red blood cell turnover and gives an indication of long term status (6-8 weeks). If both are low, then it would indicate a long-term deficiency, however if GSHPx is low with a higher status plasma selenium then this may suggest a recently increased selenium status/supply and conversely a higher GSHPx status with a lower plasma selenium concentration may indicate a previous adequacy with a current deficiency or a random or pulsitile selenium intake (e.g. what is often seen with free access mineral sources).

We will briefly outline the animal approaches for each element to be investigated.

Macro elements

Calcium, magnesium, phosphorous, sodium, potassium and chloride are all macro-minerals with homeostatic regulation and it is only during clinical deficiencies that blood values fall below the normal range. For these elements urine is a good indicator of intake as if intake is in excess of requirement then urine excretion will be elevated, whereas if intake is at or below requirements then urine excretion will be low. Urine concentrations of these minerals can be corrected to creatinine concentration to take account of the dilution effect of water intake, hot weather etc.

Dietary sulphur levels can be calculated from the diet sheet and over supply can be checked via urine sampling.

Micro elements

For most trace elements (lithium heparin) plasma or serum concentrations are appropriate, but it is important to know which is being used as normal ranges and diagnostic criteria can be different. EDTA is a metal chelator and usually is inappropriate. Multi-element analysis is commonplace now. In addition to mineral concentrations which are generally indicative of short term supply, although this is dependent on the biological half-life of each element, we can use functional indicators such as enzymes and metabolites, especially if red blood cell related (e.g. GSHPx) or stored to give a longer term indication of status (vitamin B12).

Vitamin B12 concentrations are the functional indicator relevant to cobalt supply; cobalt is not used by the animal but is utilised in the rumen for synthesis of vitamin B12, so for effective B12 production a sustained supply of cobalt is required. Although not actually required by the animal, cobalt can be used as an indicator, cobalt levels can easily be raised by increased cobalt intake/supplementation without necessarily being available for incorporation in vitamin B12. Therefore a high value is not necessarily indicative of sufficiency. However, if the level is low then this can indicate a prolonged low cobalt status and without any other direct vitamin B12 supplementation is likely to indicate a cobalt problem.

Copper also has enzymes which aid analysis of status, with erythrocyte superoxide dismutase able to give a longer term indicator of status and caeruloplasmin activity giving an indication of function (or acute phase response) which can in certain situations be linked to plasma concentrations to estimate thiomolybdate interactions.

Iron in plasma or serum is hugely influenced by haemolysis and ruminants do not generally tend to have issues with iron deficiency.

Iodine is the trace element that tends to be different; iodine cannot be meaningfully assessed directly in plasma or serum, but can be used after an extraction protocol as plasma inorganic iodine (Pii) which gives an indication of intake. Pii was originally developed to replace urine iodine as a measure as urine samples were considered hard to collect. If urine can be collected (e.g. stimulated cow) then urine iodine is a cheaper alternative to Pii which also only indicates iodine intake. Although previously thyroid hormones have been used as indicators of iodine status these have fallen out of vogue and further work on determination of iodine status is required.

One additional note for interpretation is to use diagnostic criteria or normal ranges rather than reference ranges. Reference ranges are determined by the statistical distribution of samples submitted to the lab and are not related to appearance of clinical signs or loss in performance.

Once there is an identified clinical deficiency or a defined a risk of a problem, then correction options can be explored. Options include direct to animal supplements (e.g. Drench, Bolus, Injection), which are useful in grazing situations; in feed supplement, which is useful if the animal is fed; and changing management to manage mineral issues/risks.

Although this approach should be common sense and widely used, often it isn't. This suggests a need for increased training of vets, nutritional advisers and even farmers in mineral/nutritional audit and investigation.

Conclusion

A team approach should be taken to assess nutritional status of ruminant herds/flocks. Feed availability, quality (energy and protein), water quality and availability, and flock/herd health problems should be investigated before minerals. Mineral status can be investigated by a full audit of the diet fed, including forages, grazing (analyse) and other feed inputs, and must include current and historical supplements/treatments. This or clinical signs may prompt targeted investigation of animal status via blood, liver or urine.

4

Techniques For Monitoring, Detection And Diagnosis Of Metabolic Problems In Dairy Cattle

A. MACRAE, L. BURROUGH, V. AMBRIZ-VILCHIS AND J. FORREST

Dairy Herd Health and Productivity Service (DHHPS), The Royal (Dick) School of Veterinary Studies and the Roslin Institute, the University of Edinburgh, Easter Bush Veterinary Centre Roslin, EH25 9RG

Introduction

"Metabolic diseases" are conditions in which normal metabolic processes are disturbed, and a resulting absence or shortfall or excess of a normal metabolite causes disease. Metabolic diseases of livestock are caused by productivity practices when the body reserves of calcium, magnesium or energy cannot meet the metabolic demands. In cattle, metabolic diseases usually include ketosis / fatty liver / negative energy balance, hypocalcaemia (milk fever), hypomagnesaemia (grass staggers) and subacute rumen acidosis (SARA). Trace elements are not included, and have been covered in greater detail by other chapters in these conference proceedings. This chapter will concentrate primarily on the monitoring and diagnosis of metabolic problems relating to negative energy balance and rumen health, and major mineral issues (calcium and magnesium) will be briefly covered where appropriate.

Traditional assessment of nutritional adequacy in most farm animal species has focused on inputs: the farm has a supply of feedstuffs (for example silages), whose quality has been partially assessed using feed analyses. Various cow factors, such as milk yield, live weight, and stage of lactation, are then used to determine Dry Matter Intake and nutritional requirements for the average cow in the group. A ration is then formulated, balanced with a variety of raw materials (feedstuffs) that balance the ration in terms of energy, protein and mineral requirements. This is then fed to all of the cows within the group (i.e. we assess what is [hopefully!] going into the cows), in the anticipation that it will meet their requirements.

However, it is often quoted that all dairy farms have at least four rations:

1. The ration formulated by the nutritional advisor (based on "inputs" as outlined above for the average cow on the farm or group)

2. The ration mixed and delivered in front of the cows. This may differ from ration 1 due to errors in mixing, or spoilage of feedstuffs, or unrepresentative forage analyses, or errors in calculations, over-estimation of grazed grass intakes and/ or quality etc.

3. The ration eaten by the cow. This may differ from ration 2 if feed bunk management is poor, or lack of sufficient trough space, or sorting of long forage particles from the ration, or poor cow comfort, or disease issues such as lameness – to name but a few of the common issues that might affect feed intake in dairy cows.

4. The ration digested and utilised by the cow. This may differ from ration 3 if the ration is not properly balanced, or is resulting in subacute/subclinical rumen acidosis and so rumen function is poor, or if the degradability characteristics of a feedstuff are poor and so it's nutritional content is poorly available to the animal.

In an ideal situation, all four of these rations would be identical, and the ration that was formulated by the nutritional advisor was identical to that utilised by the cow. However for the myriad of potential reasons outlined above, differences may occur which may affect nutritional intakes (a good case example of this is illustrated by Geraghty *et al.*, 2010). This may have long-term consequences for milk production, cow health and future fertility (i.e. next year's productivity).

So instead of looking at "inputs", we should really monitor "outputs" as the best indicator of what cows think of their diets. There are a range of potential parameters available to monitor (see reviews by Skidmore *et al.*, 1996; Mulligan 2012):

- Feed intake – if available from mixer wagon weigh scales, after removal of refusals.

- Milk production – peak yield, rate of decline from peak, lactation yield etc. in comparison with expected lactation curves.

- Body condition score at key stages such as late lactation, late pregnancy, early lactation etc. The aim is to keep the cows within 2.5 – 3.0 on a 5 point scale, with less than ½ unit loss of body condition in early lactation (Mulligan *et al.*, 2006; Mulligan 2012).

- Transition cow health outcomes – keeping clinical milk fever cases below 5%, left displaced abomasum (LDA) below 1%, retained foetal membranes below 10% etc.

- Scoring of rumen fill, faecal consistency and undigested feed particles in the dung (Zaaijer and Noordhuizen, 2003)

- Use of blood, urine, milk and rumen biochemistry to "ask cows what they think of their diet".

Monitoring using blood components

Metabolic profiles were first developed in the 1970s as a method of assessing nutritional status in dairy herds (Payne *et al.*, 1970), and have been utilised with modifications since (Blowey, 1975; Ward *et al.*, 1995; Whitaker, 2004). Despite slight differences in parameters measured, all metabolic profile systems involve taking blood samples from cows at key stages of the production cycle (typically late pregnancy and early lactation) and analysing for biochemical parameters that give information on cow health and potential limitations to productivity. Due to economic considerations, the aim is to provide the most amount of information from the minimum number of parameters (and thus least cost). The advantage is that metabolic profiles enable quick, accurate information on metabolic status at key stages, pinpointing constraints and enabling rapid corrective action.

Initial work using metabolic profiles established optimum values based on population distributions (Payne *et al.*, 1970). However subsequent work derived optimum values and thresholds on the basis of research work that has shown effects on cow health, fertility and productivity (for example Whitaker *et al.*, 1993; Miettinen and Setala 1993). Recent work from North America has focused on thresholds with reference to clinical disease and production, especially in association with assessment of energy balance using parameters such as β-hydroxybutyrate (BOHB) and non-esterified fatty acids (NEFA). Cows with elevated NEFA levels in the last 10 days of pregnancy are at an increased risk of developing LDA, retained foetal membranes (RFM), culling before 60 days in milk and reduced milk production in early lactation (LeBlanc *et al.*, 2005; Ospina *et al.*, 2010a, b, c; Chapinal *et al.*, 2011). Elevated NEFA and BOHB levels in the first two weeks of lactation have been associated with an increased risk of LDA, clinical ketosis, endometritis and lowered milk production in early lactation (Ospina *et al.*, 2010a, b, c; Chapinal *et al.*, 2011; reviewed by LeBlanc 2010). In relation to thresholds for minerals and trace elements, there is significant experimental work available to show responses in terms of reduced productivity, feed intake and/or signs of clinical disease when levels fall outside critical thresholds (for example Kelly 1998, Underwood and Suttle 1999).

The basic approach of the Dairy Herd Health and Productivity Service (DHHPS) for metabolic profile analysis has been described previously (Whitaker 2000; Whitaker 2004). To summarise, farmers were requested to present 17 cows in total for blood sampling in late pregnancy (ideally within 10 days of their predicted calving date), early lactation (10 – 20 days calved) and mid lactation (90 – 150 days calved), with a minimum of 5 cows in each group. Farmers and veterinary surgeons were instructed that any cows with evidence of clinical disease problems were not to be presented for blood sampling, as this would not give accurate information on the nutritional status of the animal. At the same time as blood sampling, cows were body condition scored on a 1 to 5 scale (DEFRA 2001). Details were also collected of calving dates, lactation numbers and daily milk yields for each cow sampled.

Blood samples were taken by the private veterinary surgeon using the appropriate anticoagulant for separation of plasma (oxalate fluoride for glucose analysis, and lithium heparin for all other metabolites), and transported to the DHHPS laboratory for analysis within 7 days following collection.

A standard DHHPS metabolic profile test included biochemical analysis using plasma samples for BOHB, glucose, NEFA, urea-nitrogen (urea-N), albumin, globulin, magnesium and inorganic phosphate. Additional analyses for copper and glutathione peroxidase (GSHPx) were performed only if requested by the farmer or private veterinary surgeon. Samples were analysed using an Instrumentation Laboratory IL600 wet chemistry system using reagents supplied by Randox (BOHB and GSHPx), Alpha Laboratories (NEFA) and Instrumentation Laboratory (all other metabolites). Quality assurance was provided using internal quality controls [SeraChem Level 1 and Level 2 (Randox), Seronorm (Sero) and Human Assay Multisera Level 2 (Randox)] during every metabolic profile test, and independent external quality assessment was performed once every two weeks (Randox International Quality Assessment Scheme).

Biochemical results, individual cow data and ration details were inputted into a database (Microsoft Access 2003), with subsequent analysis using Excel and Minitab 15. This work has been published by Macrae *et al.*, (2012). Optimum values for plasma metabolites in dairy cattle are given in Table 1.

Table 1. Optimum values for concentrations of plasma metabolites in dairy cattle (based on LeBlanc 2010, Ospina et al. 2010b, Ospina et al. 2010c, Whitaker 2004)

Metabolite	Lactating cows	Dry cows
β-hydroxybutyrate	< 1.0 mmol/l	< 0.6 mmol/l
Non-esterified fatty acids	< 0.7 mmol/l	< 0.4 mmol/l
Glucose	> 3.0 mmol/l	
Urea-N (urea)	> 1.7 mmol/l	
	(corresponding urea value is > 3.6 mmol/l)	
Albumin	> 30 g/l	
Globulin	< 50 g/l	
Magnesium	> 0.8 mmol/l	
Phosphate	> 1.4 mmol/l	
Plasma copper	> 10 µmol/l	
GSHPx	> 50 Units/g Hb	

Background information

In the period from April 2006 to March 2011 inclusive, a total of 2,980 metabolic profile blood tests were performed by DHHPS (an average of 596 tests per year). These samples came from 1,203 separate farms, and this dataset includes samples from 42,734 individual cows over the 5 year period.

The mean herd size was 211 cows (range 40 to 1300 cows). The mean lactation milk yield was 8,068 kg (range 4,000 to 12,327 kg), with mean butterfat of 3.98% and mean milk protein of 3.2%. Approximately 99% of herds sampled were Holstein-Friesian. Samples were obtained from herds distributed throughout the UK.

Of the metabolic profile blood tests, 54% were obtained from DHHPS members who pay an annual fee allowing them to test as necessary throughout the year. These tests were more likely to comprise routine herd blood sampling to monitor nutritional status. The remaining 46% were "one-off" individual herd tests, which were more likely to be for investigation of herd health problems with a suspected nutritional origin.

Energy balance

Assessment of energy balance was made using BOHB, NEFA and glucose. This assessment showed that approximately 30% of cows in the first 50 days of lactation had BOHB levels greater than 1.0 mmol/l (Figure 1). Of these cows with elevated BOHB, 28% of cows had evidence of subclinical ketosis (BOHB values between 1.0 – 2.9 mmol/l), and 3-4% of cows had BOHB values over 3.0 mmol/l which would be considered compatible with a diagnosis of clinical ketosis (Peek and Divers 2008; Oetzel 2004; McArt et al., 2012). 27% of cows in the last 10 days precalving had NEFA values over 0.4 mmol/l, and 47% of cows had NEFA values over 0.7 mmol/l in the first 20 days of lactation. The proportion of cows with plasma glucose values less than 3.0 mmol/l more closely mirrored the pattern seen with NEFA values, with the greatest proportion of cows affected in the first 50 days of lactation (Figure 1).

Different combinations of energy parameters are shown in Figure 2. The solid black bars represent those cows with elevated BOHB and/or NEFA results, the grey bars represent those cows with one or more of the three measures of energy balance outwith the optimum range, and the white bars are those cows with all three measures of energy balance within the optimum range. 30% of cows sampled within 10 days of calving and 20 – 30% of cows in the first 20 days of lactation had normal energy parameters, a figure comparable to previous studies (Macrae et al., 2006).

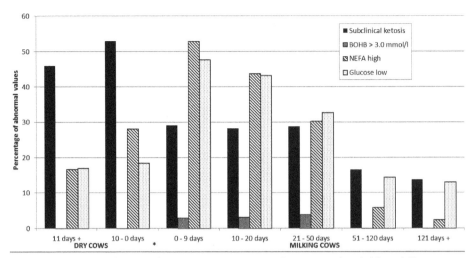

Figure 1. Percentage of cows with energy parameters outwith optimum thresholds at different stages of the lactation cycle. Subclinical ketosis is defined as BOHB values between 0.6 – 2.9 mmol/l for a dry cow, and 1.0 – 2.9 mmol/l for a milking cow. (Figure courtesy of BCVA: Macrae *et al.*, 2012)

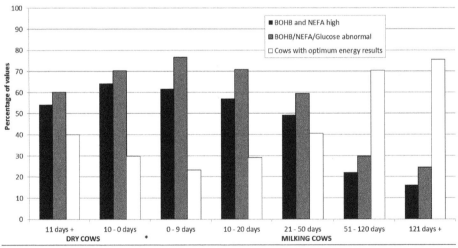

Figure 2. Percentage of cows with combinations of energy parameters outwith optimum thresholds at different stages of the lactation cycle. Black bars are cows with elevated BOHB and/or NEFA; grey bars are cows with one or more of the three measures of energy balance outwith the optimum range; white bars are those cows with satisfactory energy balance. (Figure courtesy of BCVA: Macrae *et al.*, 2012)

Protein balance

Urea-N (or urea) is a reflection of short-term intakes of Effective Rumen Degradable Protein (ERDP) from the diet, as well as the utilisation of ammonia in the rumen to form microbial protein. Urea-N results below 1.7 mmol/l (equivalent to urea levels below 3.6 mmol/l) may therefore be a reflection of a shortage of ERDP in the diet, reduced feed intake, imbalance of energy and protein supply to rumen microbes. 30% of cows in late pregnancy and the first 20 days of lactation had low urea-N values (Figure 3). However only 10% of cows over 50 days into lactation had low urea-N values, which would be more suggestive of issues with the ERDP content of the milking cow ration.

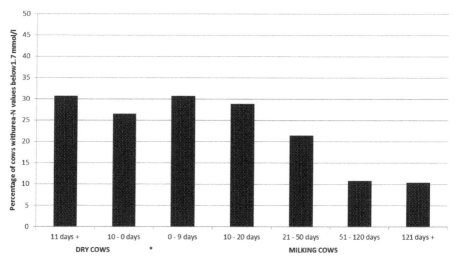

Figure 3. Percentage of cows with urea-N concentrations below 1.7 mmol/l (corresponding to urea concentrations below 3.6 mmol/l) at different stages of the lactation cycle. (Figure courtesy of BCVA: Macrae *et al.*, 2012)

Butler (1998) suggested that urea-N values over 19 mg/dl (equivalent to 3.3 mmol/l urea-N) had detrimental effects on fertility, although this is controversial (Laven and Drew 1999). 9.6% of samples in this dataset had urea-N values over 3.3 mmol/l.

3.5% of cows sampled had low albumin values, and these were usually associated with clinical disease problems in individual cows (as albumin is a negative acute phase protein in cattle). Low albumin values can also be associated with inadequate long-term protein status or impaired liver function. 10.9% of samples had globulin values over 50 g/l, which would indicate a chronic inflammatory problem such as metritis, mastitis or lameness. Chronic liver fluke and chronic suppurative pneumonia may also result in elevated globulin results.

Mineral and trace element status

Of the major minerals routinely analysed, 6% of dry cows in late pregnancy had low magnesium values, which may predispose them to hypocalcaemia at calving (Kelly 1988)(Figure 4). Apart from a peak of low magnesium and phosphate values in cows less than 10 days after calving (which is likely to be associated with reduced DM intake immediately after calving), less than 10% of milking cows showed low magnesium or phosphate results.

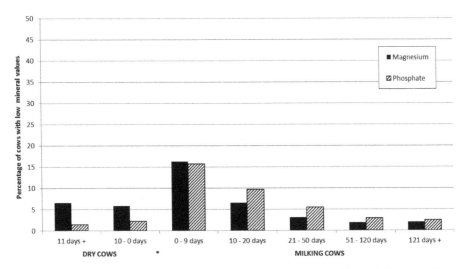

Figure 4. Percentage of cows with low magnesium (below 0.80 mmol/l) and phosphate (below 1.4 mmol/l) concentrations at different stages of the lactation cycle. (Figure courtesy of BCVA: Macrae *et al.*, 2012)

The DHHPS does not routinely measure calcium levels in submitted blood samples. This is because blood calcium levels are kept under tight homeostatic control via a series of hormone mechanisms involving parathyroid hormone and Vitamin D. Values only normally drop in the period around calving, when clinical hypocalcaemia (milk fever) may develop. Blood calcium levels below 1.5 mmol/l are considered diagnostic for clinical milk fever, but research is more controversial over the occurrence and effects of subclinical hypocalcaemia. Subclinical hypocalcaemia is defined as subnormal blood calcium levels (below 1.8 – 2.0 mmol/l) with the absence of any clinical signs of milk fever (e.g. recumbency) within 48 hours of calving. Biochemical testing has shown that around 50% of multiparous cows (parity 2+) had subnormal blood calcium levels (Reinhardt *et al.*, 2011), but whether this subclinical hypocalcaemia results in harmful effects for the cow has not been fully elucidated (Goff 2008; Jawor *et al.*, 2012). Others argue that low blood calcium levels around calving are a normal physiological mechanism as the cow's metabolism adapts to milk production at calving, and are seldom harmful provided that they do not fall too low for prolonged periods. For cows on "full" DCAB systems to control hypocalcaemia, assessment of urine pH is the preferred method of assessing acid-base balance and the degree of metabolic acidosis induced (Husband 2005).

Plasma copper analyses were performed on 27,753 individual cow samples between April 2006 and March 2012. However there is a large amount of individual animal variation in plasma copper results, and group mean values should therefore be used for interpretation (Underwood and Suttle 1999). The marginal band used by Underwood and Suttle (1999) for the interpretation of plasma copper in cattle is 6-10 µmol/l, and 3.6% of the group mean values were below 10 µmol/l indicating possible issues with copper deficiency. Only three group mean values from two different herds (0.05%) had group mean plasma copper values below 6 µmol/l, which would indicate a "high probability of current or future dysfunction and impairment of health or production" (Underwood and Suttle 1999). 0.5% of the group mean plasma copper results were over 20 µmol/l, a level which would raise potential queries over the possibility of chronic copper poisoning. However this is not diagnostic, and would need to be confirmed by liver enzyme analyses or liver/kidney copper analyses in each case.

A total of 28,200 samples between April 2006 and March 2012 were analysed for GSHPx, which is a measure of long-term selenium status (Underwood and Suttle 1999). 0.8% of these samples showed GSHPx results below 50 units per gram of Haemoglobin, indicating poor long-term selenium status. It is of note that 1st lactation heifers had significantly more low GSHPx results compared to multiparous cows (2.1% vs 0.4%; primiparous vs multiparous; $P<0.001$, Chi-squared test), and that early lactation cows had significantly more low GSHPx results compared to dry cows and mid lactation cows (0.93% vs 1.11% vs 0.46%: Dry vs Early lactation vs Mid lactation). Given that GSHPx measures long-term selenium status over the previous 2-4 months, the significant increase in the number of low GSHPx results in the early lactation group (predominantly within the first month after calving) is a reflection of poorer levels of mineral supplementation during late pregnancy in some herds. However it should be noted that 99% of all cows tested had satisfactory GSHPx results.

Monitoring using milk components

Although considered the "gold standard" as far as assessment of energy balance in dairy cattle is concerned, one major limitation of blood sampling cattle to assess nutritional status is the taking of the blood sample (usually only performed by veterinary surgeons) and time delay before subsequent analysis. Although development of "cow-side" meters to measure BOHB and glucose levels in blood (e.g. Precision

Xtra) has reduced some of these issues, research has focused on development of other methods. For example techniques to assess nutritional status via milk components would be less invasive, and less disruptive for farm routine if they could be integrated with either the milking parlour (for example in robotic milking units) or monthly milk recording, and could be performed on a more regular basis.

Measurement of ketone bodies in milk has been possible for many years, mainly for diagnosis of clinical ketosis using Rothera's reagent. The recent development and marketing of milk testing strips (for example Ketotest, Elanco) has enabled semi-quantitative assessment of milk ketone levels. However concentrations of ketones in milk are much lower than in blood (only 10 – 15%), and the sensitivity of the milk test strips is lower compared to blood sampling (Oetzel 2007). Recent technology has enabled quantitative measurement of ketones (BOHB and acetone) in milk using flow-injection analysis (Denis-Robichaud et al., 2014), and this could play a role in herd monitoring programmes when integrated into milk recording systems. The Herd Navigator system developed by DeLaval also measures BOHB levels in milk using an "in line" system for both robotic milking systems and conventional parlours, and such automation would enable routine monitoring of "at risk" cows. However accuracy, reliability and cost of such systems needs to be refined further before they are used widely on farms.

The alternative to directly measuring BOHB or other biochemical assessments of energy balance is to use proxy measures of metabolic status in milk samples, such as milk fat and milk protein. Milk fat concentrations increase during negative energy balance as a proportion of the fat mobilised by the cow will enter the milk, and individual values greater than 5% in Holstein Friesian cows are usually taken as evidence of excessive fat mobilisation. Milk protein concentrations lower than 3% in Holstein Friesian cows are usually taken as evidence of long-term negative energy balance, although some argue that this percentage value is affected by milk yield and dilution, and so aim for a total milk protein yield in the first recording of the lactation greater than 1 – 1.2 kg to take this into account. Combining milk fat and protein gives the Fat : Protein Ratio (FPR), with values over 1.4 indicative of negative energy balance (Mulligan et al., 2006). Some studies have therefore looked at these fat and protein measurements, and associated them with periparturient disease issues such as displaced abomasum (Geishauser et al., 1998).

However such measurements are prone to external non-nutritional influences such as genetics, milk yield and stage of lactation, especially in herds that factor their milk recording (i.e. do not milk sample each month from both the morning and afternoon milkings). Such issues may explain why large scale studies have failed to determine associations between commonly used milk recording parameters such as FPR and proxy measures of energy balance such as fertility (Madouasse et al., 2010).

There is currently no scientific evidence behind the use of the "3.2% Milk Protein Intercept" used by milk recording organisations for assessment of energy balance in dairy cows.

Further research is looking to refine assessment of energy balance using milk components (McParland *et al.*, 2012), especially the use of milk fatty acid profile (van Dorland *et al.*, 2011). Milk fatty acids can be derived from four major pathways: the diet, the mammary gland (de-novo synthesis), the rumen, and body fat mobilization. Therefore during negative energy balance, some long-chain fatty acids will increase due to increased body fat mobilisation (predominantly C18:0 and C18:1 cis-9), whereas other fatty acids may reduce due to nutrient and energy deficiency. Short and medium-chain fatty acids (up to C16) increase in early lactation, associated with the decline in negative energy balance (Van Haelst *et al.*, 2008; Gross *et al.*, 2011). This effect was seen also to a lesser extent in cows undergoing negative energy balance at later stages of lactation.

Correlations between energy balance and the proportion of C18:1 cis-9 fatty acids have been shown to range from 0.77 (van Haelst *et al.*, 2008) to 0.92 (Gross *et al.*, 2011). These results suggest that a high proportion of long-chain fatty acids (especially if combined with lower proportions of short and medium-chain fatty acids) and especially a high proportion of C18:1 cis-9 in milk fat can be considered as good predictors of subclinical ketosis (Van Haelst *et al.*, 2008). However similar issues arise with the use of milk fatty acid monitoring in that stage of lactation; milk yield and dietary components will alter the composition and balance of fatty acids present in milk, and therefore any analysis must be able to take such factors into account when predicting energy balance in dairy cows.

Monitoring rumen health

Dairy cow diets designed to meet the high energy demands of lactation in modern high yielding cows have necessarily involved generation of energy dense diets. Such diets contain relatively high levels of fermentable carbohydrates, which can potentially affect rumen health by lowering rumen pH, resulting in Subacute Rumen Acidosis (SARA) which may have harmful effects on cow health and productivity.

Diagnosis and monitoring of SARA is not straightforward in a dairy herd, and relies on analysis of a range of four different parameters in a herd (Grove-White 2004; Aitkinson 2009): ration assessment, cow assessment, production records, rumen sampling.

1. Ration Assessment. Table 2 highlights the main parameters used in ration formulation that are considered as risk factors for SARA:

Table 2. Risk factors for sub-acute rumen acidosis (SARA) based on ration formulation

Ration assessment	Threshold for potential risk of SARA
Concentrate : Forage Dry Matter ratio	Greater than 60 : 40
Sugar content	Greater than 6 – 8%
Starch content	Greater than 18 – 20%
Neutral Detergent Fibre (NDF)	Less than 35%
NDF from Forage	Less than 18%
Parlour concentrate allocation	More than 4 kg at each milking

All parameters used routinely in UK ration formulation assess "inputs", rather than "outputs" previously discussed. Therefore the main risk factors for SARA (supply of excess fermentable carbohydrate, or failure of the rumen buffering system) can occur in diets that appear satisfactory on paper but may result in SARA due to issues such as short particle size, sorting of effective long fibre from the ration, excessive processing of the diet, poor transition cow management etc. Likewise many nutritional advisors have experience of farms where forage intakes are poor as stocks are in short supply and/or levels of starch in the diet appear excessive. Such diets may appear to be a high risk in theory, yet cows have no obvious signs of SARA.

2. Cow Assessment. This comprises a range of clinical signs (also known as "Cow Signals") that are used to pick up the clinical signs of SARA in a herd. Classic signs of SARA in a dairy herd would be loose / variable dung consistency, fibrin casts in the faeces, faecal soiling of the cows, rumen hypomotility, cows with reduced appetite, reduced feed intake, cows "dropping their cud" when ruminating, reduced cudding activity, reduced feed efficiency as the rumen is not functioning properly resulting in the presence of undigested food material in the dung of cows, poor cow body condition and the presence of other production diseases (such as LDA, ketosis, sole haemorrhages and lameness). For further reading see reviews by Grove-White (2004) and Atkinson (2009).

Increased automated monitoring of cow signals would be beneficial in larger herds, and use of rumination collars (for example SCR Engineers, Israel) in commercial herds is now common practice. These devices use a microphone placed against the neck to detect the characteristic sounds of rumination. In a recent study comparing outputs from rumination collars against direct visual observations of cow behaviour in a commercial dairy herd, collar outputs were highly correlated with rumination in housed cows (Ambriz-Vilchis *et al.*, 2015). However in cows outside at grass, there was much less agreement between rumination collars and cow behaviour.

Despite their commercial availability and use on UK dairy farms, there remain a number of key scientific questions about the use of rumination collars on commercial dairy farms. How many cows need to be monitored each day using rumination collars to give a representative assessment of the herd? How do cow factors such as parity, stage of lactation, diseases such as lameness etc. affect rumination time? What are the thresholds that should be used to assess rumination time (ie. what should be regarded as a problem that requires action by the farmer)? Does the type of diet fed affect rumination time?

3. Production Records. Cows with SARA will typically not produce as much milk as they are expected to, and milk quality (especially the amount of butterfat) will be reduced. This lower butterfat yield is thought to be dependent on acetate production in the rumen, which in turn reflects intake of dietary fibre. Using individual cow milk recording data, it is often stated that if more than 10% of cows have butterfat concentrations below 2.5%, this is indicative of SARA in Holstein-Friesian cows. In herds that do not milk record, bulk tank butterfat concentration below 3.5 – 3.6% would be considered suggestive of SARA, although this is affected by milk yield, genetics of the cow and other non-nutritional factors.

Herds with SARA also tend to have higher levels of production diseases such as LDA, ketosis, sole haemorrhage and lameness, and poorer fertility. Such conditions are considered multifactorial and are not diagnostic of SARA, but would be indicative of potential problems with rumen health.

4. Rumen Sampling. Given the description of "rumen acidosis", it would be intuitive that measuring rumen pH in the cow would be the main method for diagnosis of SARA. The usual threshold proposed in the literature is a rumen pH of less than 5.5 in 25% of cows sampled, measured approximately 4 – 10 hours after feeding in a group of at least 12 cows. Values between pH 5.5 – 5.8 are considered marginal, and values greater than pH 5.8 are considered negative for SARA (Enemark 2009). Sampling should be standardised for time of day, time relative to feeding and stage of lactation to ensure consistency, and samples must be analysed within one hour of collection to prevent equilibration with the air and artificial alterations in pH measurements.

There are two main methods of collecting rumen fluid for pH sampling: using an oro-ruminal tube passed through the mouth, or rumenocentesis (using a needle to sample from the ventral sac of the rumen). Sampling using an oro-ruminal tube is prone to bicarbonate contamination from saliva during collection, and which area of the rumen is sampled cannot be ascertained accurately. Therefore the recommended technique for collection of rumen fluid is rumenocentesis (Duffield et al., 2004; Enemark 2009). A recent UK study has shown that 26.2% of cows had rumen pH ≤ 5.5 at one timepoint measured using rumenocentesis, and 3 out of 8 herds had greater than 25% of cows sampled with a rumen pH ≤ 5.5 (Atkinson 2014). This result is similar to other studies using rumenocentesis.

However such monitoring of rumen pH at single timepoints is very simplistic, and does not take into account the dynamics and changes in rumen pH over the day that occur in response to feed intake, consumption of large amounts of parlour concentrate in "slugs", rumination behaviour etc. More subjective measurements of rumen function from rumen fluid samples can be made by looking at protozoal size, protozoal activity and methylene blue test (Enemark 2009). However the objective must be to measure rumen pH dynamics over prolonged periods of time, and this requires either continuous measurement of rumen pH or repeated rumen fluid sampling (only possible in research centres with fistulated cows).

Technology has resulted in the development of indwelling rumen pH boluses (Mottram *et al.*, 2008), which will measure rumen pH continuously (usually every 15 minutes). Data are downloaded via wireless technology. Current lifespan of the rumen pH boluses in the cow is limited by sensor accuracy to a period of around 100 days. Deployment of rumen pH boluses in cows shows rumen pH to be a very dynamic process within the cow (Figure 5), with wide fluctuations during the day as a result of factors such as feeding behaviour and rumination activity.

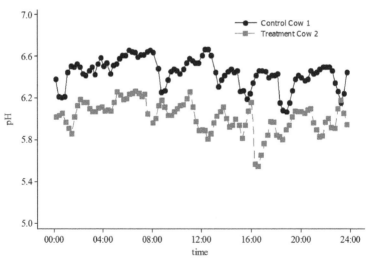

Figure 5. Rumen pH in two individual cows measured every 15 minutes over a 24 hour period using intra-ruminal pH boluses (eCow Ltd).

Adoption of such technology remains in its early stages, and aside from cost and practicalities of bolus use on commercial farms, again some key scientific questions remain. What is the best metric to measure rumen pH in a cow to assess rumen function? Options include mean pH per day, maximum and minimum rumen pH, and time during day when rumen pH ≤ 5.8. What is the link between rumen pH dynamics in a cow and rumen function? What is the individual animal variation in rumen pH that occurs due to variations in animal factors such as feed intake and body condition? How many cows do you need to measure rumen pH within a herd and/or group to provide a representative meaningful assessment of rumen health and nutrition? Until some of these fundamental questions are answered, the use of such technology on commercial farms will remain limited.

Conclusions

Clinical metabolic diseases remain relatively uncommon in UK dairy herds compared to mastitis and lameness (clinical ketosis and LDA levels below 1%, hypocalcaemia cases below 5%). However evidence would suggest that subclinical ketosis affects approximately 30% of cows in early lactation, and SARA (as assessed by rumenocentesis using conventional thresholds) affects around 20% of cows. Recent research has highlighted that such metabolic problems can have potentially harmful effects on cow health (such as increased risks for development of periparturient disease issues such as metritis, LDA and involuntary culling), production (including milk yield and milk quality) and future fertility.

Detection and monitoring is therefore critical to identifying such metabolic problems, and relies on the use of objective assessment of blood, (urine), milk and rumen biochemistry to "ask cows what they think of their diet". Modern technology will play a part in offering continuous assessment of parameters in the larger modern dairy herd, but it is important to understand that such monitoring tools should not be seen in isolation. For example, cows may develop biochemical indications of negative energy balance in early lactation as a result of (at least) five potential scenarios: 1) low energy density in the ration 2) inadequate intake of a diet that is sufficiently energy dense 3) poor rumen health or SARA resulting in poor digestion of the diet and utilisation of available energy 4) poor transition from late pregnancy and 5) disease issues such as lameness or metritis. Therefore any monitoring needs to take into account ration formulation, feed management on farm, dietary assessment, clinical signs in cows, assessment of blood, milk and rumen biochemistry, and production measures to get the full picture in the herd.

References

Ambriz-Vilchis, V., Jessop, N.S., Fawcett, R.H., Shaw, D.J., and Macrae, A.I. (2015) Comparison of rumination activity measured using rumination collars against direct visual observations and analysis of video recordings of dairy cows in commercial farm environments. *Journal of Dairy Science*, **98**, pp1750-1758.

Atkinson, O. (2009) Guide to the rumen health visit. In Practice, 31, pp 314-325.

Atkinson, O. (2014) Prevalence of Subacute Ruminal Acidosis (SARA) on UK dairy farms. *Cattle Practice*, **22**, pp11-9.

Blowey, R.W. (1975) A practical application of metabolic profiles. *Veterinary Record*, **97**, 324-327.

Butler, W.R. (1998) Review: effect of protein nutrition on ovarian and uterine physiology in dairy cattle. *Journal of Dairy Science*, **81**, pp22533-2539.

Chapina, l. N., Carson, M., Duffield, T.F., Capel, M., Godden, S., Overton, M., Santos, J.E. and, LeBlanc, S.J. (2011) The association of serum metabolites with clinical disease during the transition period. *Journal of Dairy Science*, **94**, 4pp4897-4903.

DEFRA (2001) Body condition scoring of dairy cows. *Publication PB6492*.

Denis-Robichaud, J., Dubuc, J., Lefebvre, D., and DesCôteaux, L. (2014) Accuracy of milk ketone bodies from flow-injection analysis for the diagnosis of hyperketonemia in dairy cows. *Journal of Dairy Science*, **97**, pp3364-3370.

Duffield, T., Plaizier, J.C., Fairfield, A., Bagg, R., Vessie, G., Dick, P., Wilson, J., Aramini, J. and, McBride, B. (2004) Comparison of techniques for measurement of rumen pH in lactating dairy cows. *Journal of Dairy Science*, **87**, pp59-66.

Enemark, J.M. (2009) The monitoring, prevention and treatment of sub-acute ruminal acidosis (SARA): A review. *Veterinary Journal*, **176**, pp32-43.

Geishauser, T.D., Leslie, K.E., Duffield, T.F. and Edge, V.L. (1998) An evaluation of protein/fat ratio in first DHI test milk for prediction of subsequent displaced abomasum in dairy cows. *Canadian Journal of Veterinary Research*, **62**, pp144–147.

Geraghty, T., O'Grady, L., and Mulligan, F.J. (2010) An investigation into reduced milk production following dietary alteration on an Irish dairy farm. *Irish Veterinary Journal*, **63**, pp689-694.

Goff, .JP. (2008) The monitoring, prevention, and treatment of milk fever and subclinical hypocalcemia in dairy cows. *Veterinary Journal*, **176**, pp50-57.

Gross, J., van Dorland, H.A., Bruckmaier, R.M. and, Schwarz, F.J. (2011) Milk fatty acid profile related to energy balance in dairy cows. *Journal of Dairy Research*, **78**, p p479 -– 488.

Grove-White, D. (2004) Rumen healthcare in the dairy cow. *In Practice*, **26**, pp88-95.

Husband, J. A. (2005) Strategies for the Control of Milk Fever. *In Practice*, **27**, pp88-92.

Jawor, P.E., Huzzey, J.M., LeBlanc, S.J. and, von Keyserlingk, M.A. (2012) Associations of subclinical hypocalcemia at calving with milk yield, and feeding, drinking, and standing behaviors around parturition in Holstein cows. *Journal of Dairy Science*, **95**, pp1240-1248.

Kelly, J.M. (1988) Magnesium and milk fever. *In Practice*, **10**, pp168-170.

Laven, R.A. and Drew, S.B. (1999) Dietary protein and the reproductive performance of cows. *Veterinary Record*, **145**, pp687-695.

LeBlanc, S. (2010) Monitoring metabolic health of dairy cattle in the transition period. *Journal of Reproductive Development*, **56 Supplement**, pp29-35.

LeBlanc, S.J., Leslie, K.E. and, Duffield, T.F. (2005) Metabolic predictors of displaced abomasum in dairy cattle. *Journal of Dairy Science*, **88**, pp159-170.

Macrae, A.I., Whitaker, D.A., Burrough, E., Dowell, A. and, Kelly, J.M. (2006) Use of metabolic profiles for the assessment of dietary adequacy in UK dairy herds. *Veterinary Record*, **159**, pp655-661.

Macrae, A.I., Burrough, E. and Forrest, .J (2012) Assessment of nutrition in dairy herds: Use of metabolic profiles. *Cattle Practice*, **20**, pp120-127.

Madouasse, A., Huxley, J.N., Browne, W.J., Bradley, A.J., Dryden, I.L., and Green, M.J. (2010) Use of individual cow milk recording data at the start of lactation to predict the calving to conception interval. *Journal of Dairy Science*, **93**, pp4677-4690.

McArt, J.A., Nydam, D.V. and, Oetzel, G.R. (2012) Epidemiology of subclinical ketosis in early lactation dairy cattle. *Journal of Dairy Science*, **95**, pp5056-5066.

McParland, S., Banos, G., McCarthy, B., Lewis, E., Coffey, M.P., O'Neill, B., O'Donovan, M., Wall, E., Berry, D.P. (2012) Validation of mid-infrared spectrometry in milk for predicting body energy status in Holstein-Friesian cows. *Journal of Dairy Science*, **95**, pp7225-7235.

Miettinen, P.V. and Setala, J.J. (1993) Relationships between subclinical ketosis, milk production and fertility in Finnish dairy cattle. *Preventative Veterinary Medicine*, **17**, 1-8.

Mottram, T., Lowe, J., McGowan, M. and, Philips, N. (2008) Technical note: A wireless telemetric method of monitoring clinical acidosis in dairy cows. *Computers and Electronics in Agriculture*, **64**, pp45-48.

Mulligan, F.J., O'Grady, L., Rice, D.A. and, Doherty, M.L. (2006) A herd health approach to dairy cow nutrition and production diseases of the transition cow. *Animal Reproduction Science*, **96**, pp331-353.

Mulligan, F.J. (2012) A herd health approach to dairy cow nutrition and production diseases of the transition and early lactation dairy cow. *Keynote Lectures and Round Table Proceedings*. 27th World Buiatrics Congress, Lisbon, Portugal.. pp 89-96

Oetzel, G.R. (2004) Monitoring and testing dairy herds for metabolic disease. *Veterinary Clinics of North America: Food Animal Practice*, **20(3)**, pp651-674.

Oetzel, G.R. (2007) Herd-level ketosis – diagnosis and risk factors. Proceedings of the American Association of Bovine Practitioners 40th Annual Conference, Vancouver, Canada. pp67-91

Ospina, P.A., Nydam, D.V., Stokol, T. and, Overton, T.R. (2010a) Association between the proportion of sampled transition cows with increased nonesterified fatty acids and beta-hydroxybutyrate and disease incidence, pregnancy rate, and milk production at the herd level. *Journal of Dairy Science*, **93**, pp3595-3601.

Ospina, P.A., Nydam, D.V., Stokol, T. and, Overton, T.R. (2010b) Associations of elevated nonesterified fatty acids and beta-hydroxybutyrate concentrations with early lactation reproductive performance and milk production in transition dairy cattle in the northeastern United States. *Journal of Dairy Science*, **93**, pp1596-1603.

Ospina, P.A., Nydam, D.V., Stokol, T. and, Overton, T.R. (2010c) Evaluation of nonesterified fatty acids and beta-hydroxybutyrate in transition dairy cattle in the northeastern United States: Critical thresholds for prediction of clinical diseases. *Journal of Dairy Science*, **93**, pp546-54.

Payne, J.M., Dew, S.M., Manston, R. and, Faulks, M. (1970). The use of a metabolic profile test in dairy herds. *Veterinary Record*, **87**, 150-158.

Peek, S.F. and Divers, T.J. (2008) Metabolic diseases. In: *Rebhun's Diseases of Dairy Cattle*. **2nd edn.** Eds TJ Divers and SF Peek. St. Louis, Saunders Elsevier. pp590-603.

Reinhardt, T.A., Lippolis, J.D., McCluskey, B.J., Goff, J.P., Horst, R.L. (2011) Prevalence of subclinical hypocalcemia in dairy herds. *Veterinary Journal*, **188**, pp122-124.

Skidmore, A.L., Brand, A., and Sniffen, C.J. (1996) Monitoring milk production: defining preset targets and execution. In: *Herd Health and Production Management in Dairy Practice*. Eds A. Brand, JPTM Noordhuizen and YH Schukken. Wageningen Pers. pp 223-281

Underwood, E..J and Suttle, N.F. (1999) *The Mineral Nutrition of Livestock*. **3rd edn**. Oxford, CABI Publishing

Van Dorland, H.A., Bruckmaier, R.M. and Schwarz, F.J. (2011). Milk fatty acid profile related to energy balance in dairy cows. *Journal of Dairy Research*, **78**, pp479-488.

Van Haelst, Y.N.T., Beeckman, A., Van Knegsel, A.T.M., and Fievez, V. (2008) Short communication: elevated concentrations of oleic acid and long-chain fatty acids in milk fat of multiparous subclinical ketotic cows. *Journal of Dairy Science*, **91**, pp4683-4686.

Ward, W.R., Murray, R.D., White, A.R., and Rees, E.M. (1995) The use of blood biochemistry for determining the nutritional status of dairy cows. In: *Recent Advances in Animal Nutrition*. Eds P. C. Garnsworthy, D. J. A. Cole. Nottingham, Nottingham University Press. pp 229-51

Whitaker, D. A., Smith, E.. J., da Rosa, G. O. and& Kelly, J. M. (1993). Some effects of nutrition and management on the fertility of dairy cattle. *Veterinary Record*, **133**, 61-64.

Whitaker, D. A. (2000). Use and interpretation of metabolic profiles. In: *The Health of Dairy Cattle*, pp. 89-107. Ed A. H. Andrews. Oxford, Blackwell Science. 89-107

Whitaker, D.A. (2004) Metabolic profiles. In *Bovine Medicine: Diseases and Husbandry of Cattle*. **2nd edn**. Eds A. H. Andrews, R. W. Blowey, H. Boyd, R. G. Eddy. Oxford, Blackwell Science. pp 804-817.

Zaaijer, D. and Noordhuizen, J.P.T.M. (2003) A novel scoring system for monitoring the relationship between nutritional efficiency and fertility in dairy cows. *Irish Veterinary Journal*, **56**. pp145–156.

5

Effects Of Essentil Oils On Rumen Fermentation And Performance In Ruminants

S. CALSAMIGLIA AND A. FERRET

Animal Nutrition and Welfare Service, Department of Animal and Food Sciences, Universitat Autònoma de Barcelona, Spain

Introduction

The European Union banned the use of antibiotic growth promoters (AGP) in animal feeds in 2006 (Directive 1831/2003/CEE). The beef sector used AGPs as means of increasing growth and/or feed efficiency, and the ban generated concern about potential effects on profitability and the prevalence of some diseases (mainly acidosis and bloat). Therefore, industry developed a strong research program together with research centres and Universities to identify alternative additives. Essential oils appear to be the natural alternative to in-feed AGPs (Kamel, 2001). Preliminary research in ruminants (Oh *et al.*, 1967 and 1968; Nagy and Tendergy, 1968) yielded promising results, but the development of effective and low cost ionophores in the early 1970s frustrated further developments in essential oils. However, after the announced ban on the use of AGP, the recognized antimicrobial activity of essential oils sparked the idea that they might be suitable alternatives to mimic the effects of in-feed antibiotics (Calsamiglia *et al.* 2006). Several review papers have summarized the effects and mechanism of action of plant extracts and essential oils on rumen fermentation and cattle performance (Calsamiglia *et al* 2007, Jouany and Morgavi, 2007; Benchaar *et al.*, 2008). After almost 10 years without AGPs in the European market, not only the beef, but also the dairy industry, are using several plant extracts and essential oils with similar objectives as AGP. In fact, the world market of phytoadditives was worth around $550 million in 2014 and is expected to grow to $675 million by 2020. The fastest growth is expected in the EU and North America, where public concerns on the use of in-fed antibiotic are greatest.

What are essesntial oils?

Essential oils are a group of organic compounds produced naturally during secondary metabolism of plants, and some of them have antimicrobial activities

(Gershenzon and Croteau, 1991). In ruminant nutrition, essential oils can be used as the whole plant, as a crude extract, as an oil extract or in a purified form either after extraction and isolation or by chemical synthesis (Gershenzon and Croteau, 1991; Cardozo *et al.*, 2004; Hristov *et al.*, 2012). Their effects depend on the active components and their concentrations. There is little room for variability with the use of pure active molecules. In contrast, when oils, extracts or whole plants are used, the actual concentration of active components becomes an important issue because concentration is affected by environmental factors such as heat and drought. This variability may affect their effectiveness as rumen modulators and animal performance. Sivropoulou *et al.* (1996) observed that the concentration of active components in oregano varied from 0.44 to 31.8 % for thymol and from 0.43 to 79.6 % for carvacrol, depending on the cultivar and processing methods. Marino *et al.* (2001) and Burt (2004) also reported large variations in the content of α–pinene (2 to 25%) and 1,8-cineole (3 to 89%), the active components in rosemary oil. This variability generates confusion and an additional difficulty in interpreting research results because the effects can be contradictory according to the content of the active component in the extract and the dose used. Therefore, at least part of the variability reported on their effects on rumen fermentation and animal performance may be attributed to the actual effective dose of the active component.

The active components of essential oils are classified in two main chemical groups that originate in different metabolic pathways and have different precursors (Figure 1): 1) Terpenoids, that have a basic unit of 5 carbons; and 2) Phenylpropanoids, with an aromatic ring with 6 carbons to which a 3-carbon chain is attached.

How do essential oils exert their activity?

The main target of most terpenes and phenylpropanes is the cytoplasmic membrane of bacteria (Dorman and Deans, 2000). The hydrophobic nature of these compounds allows them to get inserted into the cell membrane lipid bilayer, where they cause conformational changes that result in destabilization of the membrane and changes in the inter-membrane ionic gradient (Griffin *et al.*, 1999; Ultee *et al.*, 1999). Bacteria react by implementing counterbalancing mechanisms to maintain ionic balance, redirecting a major part of their energy to this objective. Although bacteria may survive the challenge, their growth rate is diminished, and in the dynamic environment of the rumen, the proportional contribution of different microbial species changes (Ultee *et al.*, 1999; Cox *et al.*, 2001). However, this is not the only mechanism of action, and disruption of the intermembrane electrolyte equilibrium though transport of ions, modification of pathways involved in synthesis of proteins responsible for the stability of the cell membrane, interaction of aldehydes with nucleic acids and proteins resulting in their inactivation, coagulation of certain cellular

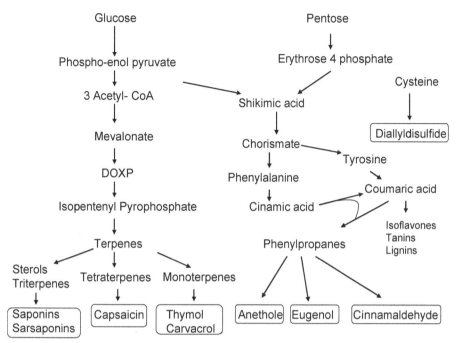

Figure 1. Metabolic pathways of biosynthesis of main plant extract active components (adapted from Calsamiglia *et al.*, 2007).

components, and interaction with enzymes, have also been suggested (Prescott *et al.*, 2004; Wendakoon and Sakaguchi, 1995; Ultee *et al.*, 2002; Gustafson *et al.*, 1997). For example, Busquet *et al.* (2005bc) suggested that the anti-methanogenic effect of garlic and its active components was the result of direct inhibition of Archaea microorganisms in the rumen. Archaea have unique membrane lipids that contain glycerol linked to long chain isoprenoid alcohols essential for stability of the cell membrane. Synthesis of the isoprenoid units in methanogenic Archaea is mediated by hydroxymethylglutaryl coenzyme A (HMG-CoA) reductase. Garlic oil and some derived organosulphur compounds are strong inhibitors of HMG-CoA reductase (Gebhardt and Beck, 1996) and, as a result, synthesis of the isoprenoid unit is inhibited, the membrane of Archaea becomes unstable, and the cells die (Figure 2). Miller and Wolin (2001) provided further support for this hypothesis by demonstrating that lovastatin and mevastatin, which decrease cholesterol production in human liver cells by inhibiting HMG-CoA reductase, specifically inhibit rumen methanogenic Archaea.

In most of these mechanisms, access to the cell membrane is an essential part of the process, and the lack of an external cell wall protection in Gram-positive bacteria makes them more sensitive to the effects of essential oils (Chao and Young, 2000;

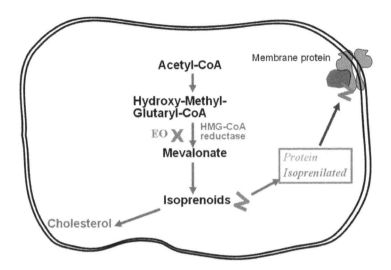

Figure 2. Proposed mechanism of action for some garlic derivatives (Busquet *et al* 2005bc) that interact with the Hydroxy-methyl-Glutaryl-CoA reductase inhibiting the synthesis of an isoprenoid critical for ancoring membrane proteins in Archea, the main methanogenic microorganisms in the rumen

Cimanga *et al.*, 2002). As mentioned above, the outer membrane surrounding the cell wall of gram-negative organisms is hydrophilic and prevents entry of lipophilic substances into the cell. Like monensin, most essential oils are lipophilic and cannot penetrate the lipopolysacharide structure of the external cell wall of Gram-negative bacteria (Cox *et al.*, 2001; Cimanga *et al.*, 2002). However, gram-negative bacteria are not totally impermeable to hydrophobic substances and low molecular weight molecules could slowly diffuse through the lipopolysaccharide layer (Griffin *et al.*, 1999; Dorman and Deans, 2000). This is the case for some aromatic hydrocarbons, such as cinnamaldehyde, carvacrol or thymol (Helander *et al.*, 1998). The ability of some small molecular weight essential oils to penetrate the external cell wall makes them excellent disinfectants and antimicrobials. However, the wide spectrum of action limits specificity of these compounds, making a selective modulation of rumen microbial fermentation more difficult.

The rumen is a microbial fermentation chamber where microbes need to develop their fermentative activity, an essential process for ruminants, and antimicrobials are not necessarily good for ruminants. For this reason, not only the activity, but also the dose, has become a critical issue in the use of essential oils in ruminants. Most research has focussed on identification of essential oils molecules that would be specific enough, and with a reasonable margin of security, to guarantee a change in fermentation profile without affecting nutrient fermentation and total volatile fatty acid (VFA) production. On the other hand, effectiveness of essential oils is affected by environmental conditions. In general terms, the susceptibility of bacteria to the antimicrobial effects of essential oils seems to increase with decreasing pH. Juven *et al.* (1994) suggested that the pH-induced change in activity of essential oils may be due to variation in the distribution of non polar phenolics between bacterial cytoplasmic membrane and the aqueous environment. For example, at low pH, thymol is mostly in the undissociated form which is more hydrophobic, allowing it to be fixed better to non-polar regions of membrane proteins and easily dissolved in the lipid phase of the bacterial membrane. Similar effects of pH on the polar-non polar configuration of other essential oils have been described and likely explain the different efficiencies of some of them under different pH environments (Tassou *et al.*, 1995; Cardozo *et al.*, 2005).

Uses and effects of essential oils in cattle

Manipulation of ruminal fermentation should be understood as an optimization process where availability of energy and protein for the animal needs to be maximized. This objective needs to be monitored carefully because achievement of one objective may come with side-effects that reduce efficiency of another process. For example, reduction in methane concentration and/or acetate to propionate ratio comes often with a reduction in total VFA production (Busquets *et al.*, 2005bc). In this case, improved retained energy due to a more efficient fermentation profile is counterbalanced by an overall reduction in digestibility, reducing energy availability for the animal. Therefore, it is important to have a good understanding of the main processes in an integrated manner.

Effects on rumen energy metabolism

Dietary carbohydrates are degraded first to pyruvate, and then fermented to VFA, CO_2 and CH_4. These reactions produce energy for microbial use (ATP) and the carbon required for microbial growth. The VFA produced are absorbed through the ruminal wall and provide energy for the cow. Optimization of fermentation requires that total VFA production is increased or maintained, and that the fermentation profile maximizes retention of energy. Efficiency of energy retention from hexoses for the animal is 63% for acetate, 109% for propionate, 78% for butyrate and 0% for methane. Therefore, a fermentation profile that increases propionate production at the expense of methane and acetate retains more metabolizable energy for the cow. The balance among different VFA is driven by the need to balance metabolic hydrogen production and utilization. The degradation process of glucose to pyruvate and fermentation to acetate produces hydrogen. In contrast, production of methane, butyrate and propionate consumes hydrogen (Table 1). This balance needs to be manipulated to successfully move the fermentation profile towards a more efficient fermentation. Methane is the most effective hydrogen sink, but methane is a gas that is lost through eructation and, therefore, does not provide energy to the animal (Russell and Wallace, 1988). Propionate and, to some extent butyrate, are alternative pathways for use of hydrogen produced during carbohydrate degradation, and retain more energy for the animal than either acetate or methane. Based on this principle, it seems reasonable to manipulate ruminal fermentation towards increasing production of propionate and butyrate (higher-energy hydrogen sinks), and lowering production of acetate (lower-energy molecules) and methane (unusable-energy hydrogen sink). This fermentation profile provides some advantages compared with monensin. The milk fat depression induced by monensin is due to lower production of precursors for milk fat synthesis (i.e., acetate and butyrate; Duffield and Bagg, 2000). However, most essential oils increase butyrate production, which may partially compensate for lowering acetate as a precursor for milk fat synthesis.

Table 1. Main carbohydrate fermentation reactions in the rumen

Hydrogen production	Hydrogen utilization
Hexose = 2 Pyruvates + 4H	Pyruvate + 4H = Propionate + H_2O
Pyruvate + H_2O = Acetate + CO_2 + 2H	2 Pyruvate + 4H = Butyrate + $2H_2O$
	CO_2 + 8H = Methane + $2H_2O$

A set of *in vitro* short-term batch fermentation studies were used to screen for effects of essential oils on rumen fermentation (Cardozo *et al.*, 2005; Busquet *et al.*, 2006; Castillejos *et al.*, 2006), and selected oils and their active components were studied in long-term continuous culture fermentation trials (Cardozo *et al.*, 2004; Busquet *et al.*, 2005a,b,c; Castillejos *et al.*, 2006). Data were used to identify several essential oils and active components that improved the fermentation profile in the desired direction, including garlic oil, cinnamaldehyde, eugenol, capsaicin and anethol.

In a previous review, the effects of essential oils were analyzed one by one (Calsamiglia *et al.*, 2007). In the current chapter, effects will be discussed based on the resulting fermentation profile. There are so many essential oils with different activities and effects, that one can almost ask what do you need, and there will be some essential oil doing it! For example, some essential oils increased acetate concentration and lowered propionate concentration (Castillejos *et al.*, 2006; Cardozo *et al.*, 2005). Many essential oils, mainly at higher doses, will depress fermentation, resulting in less digestion and VFA production (Cardozo *et al.* 2005; Busquets *et al*, 2005c). For example, thymol modified the acetate to propionate ratio, but also reduced total VFA production (Evans and Martin, 2000; Castillejos *et al.*, 2006). In contrast, other essential oils have been able to shift the fermentation profile towards lower acetate to propionate ratios without affecting total VFA production. Busquet *et al.* (2005a,b) observed that eugenol and cinnamaldehyde lowered acetate to propionate ratio, and increased proportion of butyrate, without reducing total VFA production. Garlic also lowered acetate and increased propionate and butyrate proportions (Busquet *et al.*, 2005b; 2006). This fermentation profile is different from that of monensin (which reduces acetate to propionate ratio and butyrate concentration) and is consistent with changes observed when methane inhibitors are supplied to rumen microbes (Martin and Macy, 1985). In fact, *in vitro* studies demonstrated that garlic and several of its active components lowered methane production (Busquet *et al.*, 2005c).

Effects observed in vivo were more variable, and size of responses smaller. A mixture of cinnamaldehyde and eugenol was reported to increase propionate and lower acetate proportions in the rumen of lactating dairy cows (Bach *et al.*, 2005). Cardozo *et al.* (2006) also reported a lower molar proportion of acetate and an increased molar proportion of propionate after supplementing beef diets with anis extract. Kung *et al.* (2003) demonstrated the effectiveness of anthraquinone in inhibiting methane production. These effects appear to be related to the ability of anthraquinone to inhibit transfer of electrons during the reduction of methyl Co-A to methane. However, lower methane production occurred together with an increase in concentration of hydrogen, which would not result in recovery of energy in VFA for utilization by the animal. In contrast, Benchaar *et al.* (2006, 2008) reported no effect of cinnamaldehyde and a mixture of essential oils on rumen fermentation profile. However, in vivo measures of rumen fermentation profile should be interpreted with caution. Concentrations of VFA in the rumen are the result of production, absorption and flow to the lower gut, which may confound interpretation of concentrations. In fact, Hall *et al.* (2015) reported that concentrations of metabolites in the rumen are not reliable indicators of diet fermentability. In any case, the scientific evidence suggests that some essential oils are able to interfere in the fermentation process at different levels, and may provide a useful tool to enhance energy utiliation in ruminants.

Effects on rumen N metabolism

Microbial protein is the main supplier of amino acids to the small intestine of ruminants. Proteins degraded by rumen bacteria provide amino acids and ammonia N for microbial protein synthesis. Ammonia N is the main source of N for ruminal bacteria but, in most commonly fed diets, ammonia is in excess of the capacity of rumen bacteria to use it, resulting in ammonia accumulation, absorption and losses via urine. Efficiency of N utilization in ruminants is low, and losses in the rumen account for up to 40% of total losses (Bach *et al.*, 2005; Tamminga, 1996). Therefore, it is reasonable to target protein degradation and amino acid deamination to improve dietary N utilization. Traditionally, processing feeds with heat or formaldehyde to reduce protein degradation has been the main strategy. However, with this approach availability of amino acids and ammonia for microbial growth is lower, and the increased flow of dietary protein to the small intestine is partially counterbalanced by a reduction in microbial protein synthesis (Clark *et al.*, 1992). With essential oils the strategy is to reduce deamination and/or peptidase activity. There are two distinct advantages in reducing deamination: on one hand, the amount of ammonia produced is lower; on the other hand, there is an increased concentration of amino acids for microbial use, a process that is up to 18% more efficient due to savings associated with bacterial degradation and re-synthesis of amino acids from ammonia (Wallace and Cotta, 1988). Several studies in situ (Newbold *et al.*, 2004; Molero *et al.*, 2004) observed that a mix of essential oils containing mainly thymol, eugenol, vanillin and limonene reduced protein degradation, although changes reported were small and variable depending on the feed being degraded, the type of ration fed to animals and the length of the adaptation period. McIntosh *et al.* (2000) suggested that these essential oils inhibited proteolysis. However, *in vitro* studies showed that deamination, and not peptidolytic or proteolytic activity, was the main mechanism of action of these essential oils on N metabolism (Macintosh *et al.*, 2003). Other essential oils, such as garlic, eugenol, and cinnamaldehyde, have also been shown to inhibit deamination (Busquet *et al.*, 2005a; Castillejos *et al.*, 2006). McIntosh *et al.* (2003) reported that the essential oils used in their experiments had a specific effect on a small population of rumen bacteria that were highly effective in deamination; the so-called hyper-ammonia producing bacteria (HAP). These bacteria cannot get energy from fermentation of carbohydrates and obtain energy from amino acids, releasing large amounts of ammonia-N. This hypothesis was confirmed when McIntosh *et al.* (2003) observed that pure cultures of HAP bacteria, such as Clostridium sticklandi and Peptstreptococcus anaerobius, were sensitive to addition of a mix of essential oils. However, other ammonia-producing bacteria as Prevotella ruminicola, Butyrivibrio fibrisolvens or Clostridium aminophilum were less sensitive to that mix of essential oils. Wallace *et al.* (2002) also reported that ammonia production and HAP bacteria decreased in sheep fed this mix of essential oils in a low protein diet. These effects were associated with a decrease in microbial colonization of protein feeds. In contrast, Ferme *et al.* (2004) reported that addition of cinnamaldehyde and garlic to an *in vitro* rumen simulation system resulted in a reduction in Prevotella spp., a group of bacteria known to be involved in deamination, providing evidence of a mechanism of action. In addition to deamination effects, Cardozo *et al.* (2004) observed that clove bud, with eugenol as the main active component, lowered concentrations of large peptides, small peptides and amino acids, suggesting that peptide degradation was inhibited. They suggested that combination of some essential oils with different activities at different levels in the protein degradation process (i.e., deamination and peptide degradation) may bring a synergistic effect. It appears that different essential oils may affect different reactions using different pathways. As will be discussed later, the most relevant production performance indicators have been observed when combinations of essential oils were fed.

Studies of essential oils on N metabolism in the rumen in vivo have most often shown a reduction in ammonia N concentration, although the size of effects were smaller compared with *in vitro* trials (Bach *et al*., Cardozo *et al*., 2006; Fandiño *et al*., 2008). Cardozo *et al*. (2006) also observed that capsicum oil lowered ruminal concentration of large peptides and increased concentrations of small peptides and amino acids, but had no effect on ammonia N concentrations; the combination of cinnamaldehyde plus eugenol tended to lower concentrations of branch-chained VFA and ammonia N, and increased concentrations of small peptides and amino acids, suggesting that deamination of amino acids was inhibited. In contrast, Rodríguez-Prado *et al* (2012) observed a linear increase in ammonia N concentrations when feeding increasing doses of capsicum. Benchaar *et al*. (2006) also reported that feeding this mix of essential oils to dairy cattle had no effect on N metabolism. However, as already discussed for VFA, in vivo measures of rumen fermentation profile should be interpreted with caution. Concentration of ammonia N in the rumen is the result of deamination, recycling, utilization by rumen bacteria and flow to the lower gut, so may not reflect true N metabolism in the rumen (Hall *et al*., 2015). In any case, the scientific evidence suggests that some essential oils are able to interfere in the protein degradation process at different levels, which may provide a useful tool for lowering protein degradation in the rumen.

Effects on dairy cow performance

Initially, essential oils were tested for potential effects as flavours on feed intake, assuming that increased intake would push higher production. Weller and Phipps (1989) reported that cows supplemented with a commercial product containing orange oil, dihydrocoumarin, citronella and vanillin resulted in an increase in DM intake (average of 0.7 kg/d), but milk production was not affected. It is possible that the lack of effect of higher intake on performance was due to the fact that cows were in late lactation. Nombekela *et al*. (1994) also evaluated effects of anise oil as a flavour in dairy cattle, but DM intake was not affected.

Several studies have been conducted to determine effects of essential oils on dairy cattle performance (Table 2). Overall average indicates that use of essential oils has minimum effect on animal performance. However, such simplification is unfair. For example, the most negative effects were observed at higher than recommended doses for capsicum (Hristov et al., 2013) and a blend of essential oils (Benchaar et al., 2007). With few exceptions (Kung et al., 2008; Tekkipe et al., 2013; and Hall et al., 2014), DM intake was either maintained or slightly reduced. When milk production was improved, treatments were mixtures of essential oils, which increased milk yield by 1.2 L/cow/d (Hall et al., 2014) and 1.8 L/cow/d, (Kung et al., 2008). It is likely that the synergy between essential oils may be advantageous in modulating rumen fermentation and improving animal performance. Lack of statistical significance may be attributed to small numbers of animals used for detecting a small difference in a highly variable measure. However, when positive, differences were biologically and economically relevant. A careful review of the papers in Table 2 did not identify conditions that may predispose to a better response. Neither level of production, forage used (amount or type), nor chemical composition of the diet provided clues on conditions where use of essential oils may be more successful. Bravo and Doane (2008) conducted a meta-analysis of 16 side-by-side commercial trials where a mixture of cinnamaldehyde and eugenol was supplemented to lactating dairy cows. Milk production increased by 0.9 L/d without change in feed efficiency (1.44 vs. 1.46 kg of milk/kg of DMI).

Overall, the effect of feeding essential oils to dairy cattle has resulted in wide variability of results, but when positive, a mixture of active components have been used and the response has been economically relevant. However, the factors that make such responses positive have not been identified.

Effect on beef cattle performance

The beef industry had been using AGP for a long time. The ban on their use in the European Union in 2006 prompted development of essential oils as alternatives. Although evidence from *in vitro* experiments is abundant, performance trials are limited. Table 3 summarizes the peer reviewed papers published to date on the use of essential oils for beef cattle. The active components most commonly used in these trials are cinnamaldehyde, thymol, capsicum, anis, eugenol and/or some mixtures of these essential oils.

Cinnamaldehyde was used by Yang *et al.* (2010a) in steers fed a 9 to 91 forage to concentrate diet. Authors reported a 17% increase in DM intake in the first month of the experiment. Although at the end of the experimental trial the difference was not significant, a numerical 8% increase was maintained, and live-weight gain increase numerically an average of 4% at 0.4 g/d of cinnamaldehyde. Similar results were obtained by Vakili *et al.* (2013) using cinnamaldehyde in growing Holstein bulls. Capsicum extract has been shown to consistently increase DM intake when fed at moderate doses (Cardozo *et al.*, 2006; Rodríguez-Prado *et al.*, 2012; Fandiño *et al.*, 2007), with increases ranging from 9 to 11 %, with no information about effects on live-weight gain and feed efficiency. Moreover, capsicum modified the pattern of DM intake, reducing intake in the first 2 h after feeding but increasing it thereafter. The more even distribution of intake resulted in a higher average pH and a smaller fluctuation, probably helping in to prevent development of sub-acute ruminal acidosis (Rodríguez-Prado *et al.*, 2012). Geraci *et al.* (2012) tested a mixture of cinnamaldehyde, eugenol and capsicum in steers, and reported a 16% increase in live-weight gain accompanied by a 16% numerical increase in feed efficiency, compared

Table 2. Effect of feeding essential oils on dairy cattle performance

Reference	%Forage	DMI (kg/d)	Milk (kg/d)	Milk fat (%)	Milk protein (%)	Treatment [1]	Dose
Benchaar et al. 2007	43	17.3	29.3	2.95	3.18	Control	--
	43	17.2	27.8	3.13	3.24	Mix 1	0.75 g/d
Benchaar et al. 2007	50	17.7	28.4	2.69	3.52	Control	--
	50	17.5	28.1	2.45	3.48	Mix 1	0.75 g/d
Yang et al., 2007	40	20.7	29.0	3.14	3.31	Control	--
	40	19.9	28.9	2.68	3.25	Monensin	0.32 g/d
	40	20.4	29.9	3.46	3.23	Garlic	5 g/d
	40	20.5	29.4	3.40	3.28	Juniper	2 g/d
Kung et al., 2008	58	26.4[a]	39.8[a]	2.89	3.11	Control	--
	58	28.3[b]	41.7[b]	2.99	3.07	Mix 1	1.2 g/d
Tassoul and Shaver, 2009	50	24.5	48.2	3.48	3.10	Control	--
	50	22.7	48.1	3.46	2.95	Mix 1	1.03 g/d
Spanghero et al., 2009	56	19.7	31.4	3.68	3.17	Control	--
	56	19.4	30.7	3.82	3.20	Eugenol	0.04 g/d
	56	19.5	31.2	3.70	3.23	Eugenol	0.08 g/d
	56	19.7	31.2	3.71	3.14	Eugenol	0.12 g/d
Santos et al., 2009	33	37.4	49.2	3.32	2.79	Control	--
	33	26.0	49.2	3.39	2.79	Mix 2	0.85 g/d
Benchaar et al., 2009	65	17.0	30.8	4.01	3.00	Control	--
	65	16.8	30.9	3.83	3.04	Eugenol	0.85 g/d
Benchaar et al., 2009	34	19.9	31.7	3.62	3.30	Control	--
	34	20.0	32.7	3.67	3.32	Eugenol	0.85 g/d
Tager and Krause, 2011	42	23.9	33.0	3.50	2.80	Control	--
	42	23.3	32.8	3.50	2.80	Mix 3	0.5 g/d
	42	23.2	31.6	3.40	3.50	Mix 3	10 g/d
	42	22.9	31.1	3.60	2.70	Mix 4	0.25 g/d
Tekkipe et al., 2011	60	26.7	43.6	3.12	2.79	Control	--
	60	26.0	44.1	3.29	2.96	Oregano	500 g/d
Tekippe et al., 2013	54	27.4	41.9	3.39	2.93	Control	--
	54	27.3	42.2	3.43	2.94	Mix 3	0.525 g/d
Tekippe et al., 2013	55	26.9	42.4	3.22	2.98	Control	--
	55	27.5	42.3	3.31	2.99	Mix 3	0.525 g/d
Hristov et al., 2013	62	21.2	37.4[a]	3.69	3.18	Control	--
	62	21.2	36.4[ab]	3.77	3.25	Curcumin	2 g/d
	62	19.9	35.8[ab]	3.64	3.24	Garlic	2 g/d
	62	21.3	35.2[b]	3.56	3.24	Capsicum	2 g/d
Wall et al., 2014	53	21.4	37.9	3.69	2.87	Control	--
	53	22.8	39.1	3.59	2.91	Mix 3	0.350 g/d

1 Mix 1 = Crina (Eugenol + Vanillin + Guaiacol + Limoneno; DSM Nutrition&Health, Kaiseraugst, Switzerland); Mix 2 = Agolin (Eugenol+Coriander+Geranil; Agolin SA, Geneva, Switzerland); Mix 3 = XTRACT6965 (Cinnamaldehyde + Eugenol; Pancosma P&A, Geneva, Switzerland); Mix 4 = XTRACT6933 (Capsicum oil; Pancosma P&A, Geneva, Switzerland)

with a Control treatment containing monensin. Overall, out of 15 treatments from these 10 papers, DM intake was icreased in 9, with an average 9% improvement. For live-weight gain, a numerical improvement was observed in 6 out of 10 treatments, with an average response of 5%. These improvements are relevant from the biological and economic point of view. Although there is need for additional research to identify conditions under which positive effects are more likely to be obtained, the potential improvents in live-weight gain are relevant for beef farmers.

Other uses

Change in FA profile of milk

Some preliminary studies (Lourenço *et al.*, 2005, 2007a,b) reported an increase in concentration of intermediates of the biohydrogenation of fatty acids in the rumen (i.e., C18:1 trans-11 and CLA cis-9, trans-11) after feeding botanically diverse forages compared with feeding ryegrass, and suggested that biohydrogenation of unsaturated fatty acids in the rumen was modified. In fact, the microbial population profile was modified in these animals, and authors hypothesized that secondary metabolites in these plants were responsible for changes in the rumen microflora and subsequent modification of FA biohydrogenation metabolism. To confirm the hypothesis, Lourenço *et al.* (2008) using a dual flow continuous culture system, tested effects of several plant extracts on fatty acid metabolism. Use of cinnamaldehyde resulted in accumulation of trans-10 isomers, suggesting that the metabolic pathway of C18:2 was shifted away from the normal trans-11 pathway. Moreover, overall biohydrogenation of C18:2 and C18:3 were reduced, reflected by lower concentrations of several intermediates of the trans-11 pathway (i.e., C18:1 trans-11, C18:1 trans-15 and C18:1 cis-15) and reduction in saturated fatty acids. Some degree of inhibition of the same pathways was also observed with eugenol, although the effects were smaller. More recently, Foskolos *et al.* (2015) tested the effects of propyl-propane thiosulfonate (PTSO), a stable garlic derivative, on microbial fermentation in a dual flow continuous culture system, and reported an increase in outflow of unsaturated fatty acids at the expense of saturated fatty acids.

Although these changes suggest that fatty acid profile of milk could be affected, results of feeding essential oils on fatty acid profile of milk have been inconsistent. Benchaar and Chouinard (2009) and Benchaar *et al.* (2006) reported that feeding individual or mixed essential oils had no effect on fatty acid profile of milk. In contrast, some changes were reported in other trials (Benchaar *et al.*, 2007), where concentration of conjugated linoleic acid (CLA), a health-promoting fatty acid, or unsaturated fatty acids in milk fat were increased. Foskolos *et al.* (2013) also reported a reduction in proportion of saturated (65.3 vs. 61.8%) and an increase in unsaturated (34.6 vs. 38.1%) fatty acids in milk as a result of feeding PTSO to dairy cows.

Table 3. Effect of feeding essential oils on beef cattle performance

	F:C[1]	Intake[2]	ADG[3]	FCR[4]	Treatments [5]	Doses
Devant et al.,	18:88	9.11	1.48[a]	5.02	Control	--
2007	16:84	9.10	1.57[b]	4.85	Monensin	0.25 g/d
	16:84	9.19	1.54[ab]	5.02	Mix 1	0.02 g/d
Wanapat et al.,	Ad lib	2.7% BW	--	--	Control	
2008	Ad lib	2.7% BW	--	--	Citronela	100 g/d
	Ad lib	3.0% BW	--	--	Citronela	200 g/d
	Ad lib	3.1% BW	--	--	Citronela	300 g/d
Fandiño et al.,	10:90	7.5[b]	--	--	Control	--
2008	10:90	7.6[b]	--	--	Anethol	0.5 g/d
	10:90	8.3[a]	--	--	Capsicum	0.5 g/d
	10:90	7.7[b]	--	--	Monensin	0.24 g/d
Meyer et al.,	7.5:92.5	12.1[a]	1.76	6.90[a]	Control	--
2009	7.5:92.5	12.0[a]	1.81	6.62[ab]	Mix 2	1 g/d
	7.5:92.5	12.0[a]	1.81	6.62[ab]	Mix 3	1 g/d
	7.5:92.5	11.9[a]	1.83	6.54[b]	Mix 4	1 g/d+0.09 g/d
	7.5:92.5	11.4[b]	1.78	6.41[b]	Mix 5	0.3 g/d+0.09 g/d
Yang et al.,	15:85	9.41	1.51	--	Control	--
2010a	15:85	9.56	1.27	--	Eugenol	0.4g/d
	15:85	9.88	1.25	--	Eugenol	0.8 g/d
	15:85	9.65	1.35	--	Eugenol	1.6 g/d
Yang et al.,	15:85	9.7[ab]	--	--	Control	--
2010b	15:85	10.7[ab]	--	--	Cinnamaldehyde	0.4g/d
	15:85	10.1[ab]	--	--	Cinnamaldehyde	0.8 g/d
	15:85	8.7[b]	--	--	Cinnamaldehyde	1.6 g/d
Yang et al.,	9:91	7.78	1.68	4.57	Control	--
2010c	9:91	8.42	1.74	4.78	Cinnamaldehyde	0.4 g/d
	9:91	8.17	1.65	4.85	Cinnamaldehyde	0.8 g/d
	9:91	7.69	1.64	4.59	Cinnamaldehyde	1.6 g/d
	9:91	7.92	1.2	4.48	Monensin	0.33 g/d
Geraci et al.,	16:84	0.11 kg/kg BW	1.27	3.94	Monensin	0.05 g/kg DM
2012	16:84	0.11 kg/kg BW	1.27	4.19	Mix 6 + Capsicum	0.27 + 0.13 g/d
(period 1)						
Geraci et al.,	16:84	0.14 kg/kg BW	1.23	6.49	Monensin	0.05 g/kg DM
2012	16:84	0.13 kg/kg BW	1.43	5.46	Mix 6 + Capsicum	0.27 + 0.13 g/d
(period 2)						
Rodriguez-Prado	10:90	8.56	--	--	Control	--
et al., 2012	10:90	9.84	--	--	Capsium	0.12 g/d
	10:90	8.68	--	--	Capsium	0.25 g/d
	10:90	9.40	--	--	Capsium	0.50 g/d
Vakili et al., 2012	15:85	8.0	1.19	6.62	Control	--
	15:85	8.1	1.31	6.21	Thyme	5 g/d
	15:85	7.8	1.26	6.25	Cinnamon	5 g/d

1 F:C = Forage to concentrate ratio
2 Intake = Intake as kg/d or % body weight as indicated
3 ADG = Average daily gain in kg/d.
4 FCR = Feed convertion rate in kg intake/kg gain
5 Treatments: Mix 1: Fenugreek + Artichoke + Ginseng; Mix 2: Crina (Eugenol + Vanillin + Guaiacol +
Limonene; DSM Nutrition&Health, Kaiseraugst, Switzerland); Mix 3: Guaiacol + Linalool + Alfa-pineno;
Mix 4: Mix 2 + Tylosin; Mix 5: Monensin + Tylosin; Mix 6: Cinnamaldehyde + Eugenol (Pancosma P&A,
Geneva, Switzerland)

Silage making

During the ensiling process a large proportion of plant true protein is transformed into non-protein N (Carpintero *et al.*, 1979). This process has been attributed mainly to activity of plant enzymes. However, lactic acid producing bacteria, enterobacteria and clostridia present in silages have proteolytic activity and may contribute to the process. Because some essential oils interfere with degradation of proteins in the rumen, it is reasonable to hypothesize that they may contribute to reduce such process in the silage. Kung *et al.* (2008) were the first to study potential effects of essential oils on control of proteolysis in silages. However, the low dose of a commercially available mixture of essential oils used (40 and 80 mg of essential oils/kg of fresh forage) and selection of maize (low protein) as the ensiling crop, limited the possibility of essential oils to affect protein degradation during ensiling. Chaves *et al.* (2012) tested higher doses (125 to 400 mg of essential oils/kg of fresh forage) of essential oils of cinnamon leaf, oregano and sweet orange on barley silage. Similar to maize silage, however, the low protein content of these crops limited potential effects of essential oils on silage protein degradation. To overcome these problems, Foskolos *et al.* (2010) tested effects of thymol, eugenol, cinnamaldehyde, capsaicin and carvacrol at doses ranging from 50 to 2,000 mg/kg of fresh forage on protein degradation and deamination in 2kg microsilos of a high protein fresh ryegrass. Only when the highest doses of essential oils were tested was an effect reported, resulting in a moderate increase (9.7%) in true protein N. The relatively small response, together with an excessive dose (economically unfeasible and exceeding levels recommended to be fed to dairy cows), limits the applicability of this approach.

Conclusions

Many essential oils are able to inhibit rumen microbial fermentation, confirming their antimicrobial activity. When concentration in rumen fluid *in vitro* was above 1,000 mg/L, effects were in most cases detrimental. However, when a fermentation profile consistent with better energy and protein utilization in the rumen was reported, doses ranged in most cases from 50 to 500 mg/L depending on the active compound. In most cases, propionate and butyrate proportions increased, and the acetate proportion and acetate to propionate ratio decreased, a profile consistent with inhibition of methanogenesis. Lowering of ammonia N concentration and accumulation of amino acids and small peptides indicate that the main mechanism of action for essential oils is inhibition of deamination, although inhibition of peptidolysis has also been suggested. Several performance trials in dairy and beef cattle have been published, but data are limited. However, when positive responses were reported, mixtures of essential oils were used, reflecting the need of synergies between different essential oils to result in a performance benefit. The expected size of the response (around 3 to 5%

increase in either milk production or live-weight gain) is economically relevant, but small enough and with sufficient variation to make it difficult to design experimental trials with sufficient statistical power to prove a statistically significant difference. The limited number of trials conducted to date does not allow identification of the optimal conditions of use that result in improved performance.

References

Bach, A., Calsamiglia, S., Greathead, H. and Kamel, C. (2005) Effect of a combination of eugenol and cinnamaldehyde on ruminal protein and energy metabolism in dairy cows. BOKU Symposium Tiererahrung, Wien, Austria.

Bach, A., Calsamiglia, S. and Stern, M.D. (2005) Invited review: Nitrogen metabolism in the rumen. *Journal of Dairy Science*, **88** (E. Suppl.), E9-E21.

C. Benchaar, McAllister, T.A. and Chouinard, P.Y. (2008) Digestion, ruminal fermentation, ciliate protozoal populations, and milk production from dairy cows fed cinnamaldehyde, quebracho condensed tannin, or Yucca schidigera Saponin Extracts. *Journal of Dairy Science*, **91**, 4765–4777.

Benchaar, C. and Chouinard, P.Y. (2009) Short communication: Assessment of the potential of cinnamaldehyde, condensed tannins, and saponins to modify milk fatty acid composition of dairy cows. *Journal of Dairy Science*, **92**, 3392–3396.

Benchaar, C., Petit, H. V. Berthiaume, R., Whyte, T. D. and Chouinard, P. Y. (2006) Effects of addition of essential oils and monensin premix on digestion, ruminal fermentation, milk production, and milk composition in dairy cows. *Journal of Dairy Science*, **89**, 4352–4364.

Benchaar, C., Lettat, A., Hassanat, F., Yang, W.Z., Forster, R.J., Petit, H.V. and Chouinard, P.Y. (2012) Eugenol for dairy cows fed lowor high concentrate diets: effects on ruminal fermentation characteristics, rumen microbial digestion, and milk fatty acid profile populations. *Animal Feed Science and Technology*, **178**, 139-150.

Benchaar, C., Petit, H.V., Berthiaume, R., Ouellet D.R., Chiquette J. and Chouinard P.Y. (2007) Effects of essential oils on digestion, ruminal fermentation, rumen microbial populations, milk production, and milk composition in dairy cows fed alfalfa silage or corn silage. *Journal of Dairy Science*, **90**, 886–897.

Blanck, R., Vecht, K,. Oguey, C. and Wall, E. (2014) The effects of supplementation with a blend of capsicum, cinnamaldehyde, and eugenol on milk production performance of dairy cows. *Journal of Dairy Science*, **91** (E- Suppl. 1; abstr. 1603), 785.

Bravo, D. and Doane, P. (2008) Meta-analysis of the effect of mixture of cinnamaldehyde and eugenol on dairy cattle performance. *Journal of Dairy Science*, **91**(Suppl. 1), 588

Burt, S. (2004) Essential oils: their antibacterial properties and potential applications in foods-a review. *International Journal of Food. Microbiology*, **94**, 223-253.

Busquet, M., Calsamiglia, S., Ferret, A. and Kamel, C. (2005a) Screening for the effects of plant extracts and secondary plant metabolites on rumen microbial fermentation in a continuous culture system. *Aminal Feed Science Technology*, **123-124**, 597-613.

Busquet, M., Calsamiglia, S., Ferret, A. and Kamel, C. (2006) Plant extracts affect *in vitro* rumen microbial fermentation. *Journal of Dairy Science*, **89**, 761-771.

Busquet, M., Calsamiglia, S., Ferret, A., Carro, M.D. and Kamel, C. (2005c) Effect of garlic oil and four of its compounds on rumen microbial fermentation. *Journal of Dairy Science.* **88**, 4393-4404.

Busquet, M., Calsamiglia, S., Ferret, A., Cardozo, P.W. and Kamel, C. (2005b) Effects of cinnamaldehyde and garlic oil on rumen microbial fermentation in a dual flow continuous culture. *Journal of Dairy Science*, **88**, 2508-2516.

Calsamiglia, S., Castillejos, L. and Busquet., M. (2006) Alternatives to antimicrobial growth promoters in cattle. In: *Recent Advances in Animal Nutrition*. P.C. Garnsworthy, and J. Wiseman, ed. Nottingham University Press, Nottingham, UK. 129-167.

Calsamiglia, S., Busquet, M., Cardozo, P.W., Castillejos, L. and Ferret., A. (2007) Essential oils as modifiers of rumen microbial fermentation: a review. *Journal of Dairy Science*, **379 90**: 2580-2595.

Cardozo, P. W., Calsamiglia, S., Ferret, A. and Kamel,. C. (2004) Effects of natural plant extracts on protein degradation and fermentation profiles in continuous culture. *Journal of Animal Science*, **82**, :3230-3236.

Cardozo, P.W., Calsamiglia, S., Ferret, A. and Kamel, C. (2005) Screening for the effects of natural plant extracts at different pH on *in vitro* rumen microbial fermentation of a high-concentrate diet for beef cattle . *Journal of Animal Science*, **83**, 2572-2579.

Cardozo, P.W., Calsamiglia, S., Ferret, A. and Kamel, C. (2006) Effects of alfalfa extract, anise, capsicum and a mixture of cinnamaldehyde and eugenol on ruminal fermentation and protein degradation in beef heifers fed a high concentrate diet. *Journal of Animal Science*, **84**, 2801-2808.

Carpintero, C.M., Henderson, A.R. and McDonald,. P. (1979) The effect of some pre-treatments on proteolysis during ensiling of herbage, *Grass and Forage Science*, **34**, 311-315.

Castillejos, L., Calsamiglia, S. Ferret, A. and Losa., R. (2005) Effects of a specific blend of essential oil compounds and the type of diet on rumen microbial fermentation and nutrient flow from a continuous culture system. *Animal Feed Science Technology*, **119**, 29-41.

Castillejos, L., Calsamiglia, S. Ferret, A. and Losa, R. (2007) Effects of dose and adaptation time of a specific blend of essential oils compounds on rumen fermentation. *Animal Feed Science Technology*, **132**, 186-201.

Castillejos, L., S. Calsamiglia, S. and A. Ferret. A. (2006) Effect of essential oils active compounds on rumen microbial fermentation and nutrient flow in *in vitro* systems. *Journal of Dairy Science*, **89**, 2649-2658.

Chao, S. C., and Young,. D.G. (2000) Screening for inhibitory activity of essential oils on selected bacteria, fungi and viruses. *Journal of Essential Oil Research*, **12**, 639-649.

Chaves A.V., Baah, J., Wang, Y., McAllister, T.A. and Benchaar, C. (2012) Effects of cinnamon leaf, oregano and sweet orange essential oils on fermentation and aerobic stability of barley silage. *Journal of the Science of Food and Agriculture*, **92**(4), 906-15.

Cimanga, K., Kambu, K., Tona, L., Apers, S., Bruyne, T., Hermans, N., Totté, J., Pieters, L. and Vlietinck., A.J. (2002) Correlation between chemical composition and antibacterial activity of essential oils of some aromatic medicinal plants growing in the Democratic Replublic of Congo. *Journal of Ethnopharmacology*, **79**, 213-220.

Clark, J.H., Klusmeyer Klusmeyer, T.H. and CameronCameron, M.R. (1992) Microbial protein synthesis and flows of nitrogen fractions to the duodenum of dairy cows. *Journal of Dairy Science*, **75**, 2304–2323.

Cox, S. D., Mann, C.M. and Markam,. J.L. (2001) Interaction between components of the essential oil of Melaleuca alternifolia. *Journal of Applied Microbiology*, **91**, 492-497.

Devant, M., Anglada, A. and Bach, A. (2007) Effects of plant extract supplementation on rumen fermentation and metabolism in young Holstein bulls consuming high levels of concentrate. *Animal Feed Science and Technology*, **137** (1–2), 46-57.

Dorman, H. J. D., and Deans,. S.G. (2000) Antimicrobial agents from plants:: antibacterial activity of plant volatile oils. *Journal of Applied Microbiology*, **88**, 308-316.

Duffield, T. F., and Bagg,. R.N. (2000) Use of ionophores in lactating dairy cattle: a review. *Canadian Veterinary Journal*, **41**, 88–394.

Evans, J. D., and Martin., S.A. (2000) Effects of thymol on ruminal microorganisms. *Current Microbiology*, **41**, 336-340.

Fandiño, I., Calsamiglia, S., Ferret, A. and, Blanch, M., (2008.) Anise and capsicum as alternatives to monensin to modify rumen fermentation in beef heifers fed a high concentrate diet. *Animal. Feed Science Technology*, **145**, 409-417.

Ferme, D., Banjac, M., Calsamiglia, S., Busquet , M., Kamel, C. and Avgustin,. G. 2004. The effects of plant extracts on microbial community structure in a rumen-simulating continuous-culture system as revealed by molecular profiling. *Folia Microbiologica*, **49**, 151-5.

Foskolos, A., Siurana, A., Ferret, A., Castillejos, L., Bravo, D. and Calsamiglia, S. (2013) The effect of propyl-propylthiosulphonate and capsicum addition on ruminal fermentation and animal performance of lactating dairy cows. *Journal of Dairy Science*, **96**(Suppl. 1), 505.

Foskolos, A., Siurana, A., Rodriquez-Prado, M., Ferret, A., Bravo, D. and S. Calsamiglia, S. (2015) The effects of a garlic oil chemical compound, propyl-propane thiosulfonate, on ruminal fermentation and fatty acid outflow in a dual-flow continuous culture system. *Journal of Dairy Science*, **98**, 2014-8674

Foskolos A., Cavini, S., Rodriquez-Prado, M., Ferret, A. and Calsamiglia, S. (2010) *A screening test of the use of essential oils compounds on ryegrass silage for preventing nitrogen losses in sustainable dairy production systems.* 3rd EAAP International symposium on energy and protein metabolism and nutrition Parma, Italy, 6-10 September 2010 (*poster*)

Gebhart, R., and Beck., H. (1996) Differential inhibitory effects of garlic-derived organosulfur compounds on cholesterol biosynthesis in primary rat hepatocyte cultures. *Lipids*, **31**, 1269-1276.

Geraci, J.I., Garciarena, A.D., Gagliostro, G.A., Beauchemin, K.A. and, Colombatto, D., (2012).Plant extracts containing cinnamaldehyde, eugenol and capsicum oleoresin added to feedlot catte diets: Ruminal environment, short term intake pattern and animal performance. *Animal Feed Science and Technology*, **176**, 123-130.

Gershenzon, J., and Croteau., R. (1991) Terpenoids. In: *Herbivores: their interactions with secondary plant metabolites, Vol. 1*. G. A. Rosenthal, and M. R. Berenbaum, ed. Academic Press, San Diego, CA. pp 165-219

Griffin, S.G., Wyllie, S.G., Markham, J.L. and Leach, D.N. (1999) The role of structure and molecular properties of terpenoids in determining their antimicrobial activity. *Flavour and Fragrance Journal*, **14**, 322-332.

Gustafson, R. H., and R. E. Bowen,. R.E. (1997) Antibiotic use in animal agriculture. *Journal of Applied. Microbiology*, **83**, 531-541.

Hall, M.B., Nennich, T.D., Doane, P.H. and Brink, G.E. (2015) Total volatile fatty acid concentrations are unreliable estimators of treatment effects on ruminal fermentation in vivo. *Journal of Dairy Science*, **98**, 3988-3999.

Helander, I. M., Alakomi, H., Latva-Kala, K., Mattila-Sandholm, T., Pol, I., Smid, E.J., Gorris, L.G.M. and Wright, A. (1998) Characteritzation of the action of selected essential oil components on Gram-negative bacteria. *Journal of Agricultural and Food Chemistry*, **46**, 3590-3595.

Hristov, A.N., Lee, C., Cassidy, T., Heyler, K., Tekippe, J.A., Varga, G.A., Corl, B. and Brandt, R.C. (2012) Effect of Origanum vulgare L. leaves on rumen fermentation, production, and milk fatty acid composition in lactating dairy cows. *Journal of Dairy Science*, **96**, 1189–1202

Jouany, J.P. and Morgavi, D.P. (2007) Use of natural products as alternatives to antibiotic feed additives in ruminant production. *Animal*, **1**, 1443-1466.

Juven, B. J., Kanner, J., Schved, F. and Weisslowicz, H. (1994) Factors that interact with the antibacterial action of thyme essential oil and its active constituents. Journal of Applied Bacteriology, **76**, 626-631.

Kamel, C. (2001) Tracing modes of action and the roles of plant extracts in non-ruminants. Pages 135-150 In: *Recent Advances In Animal Nutrition*. P. C. Garnsworthy, and J. Wiseman, ed. Nothingham University Press, Nothingam, UK. pp 135-150

Kung, L. Jr., Smith, K.A., Smalaga, A.M., Endress, K.M., Bessett, C.A., Ranjit, N.K. and Yaissle,. J. (2003) Effects of 9,10 anthraquinine on ruminal fermentation, total-tract digestion, and blood metabolite concentrations in sheep. *Journal of Animal Science*, **81**, 323-328.

Kung, L. Jr., Williams, P., Schmidt, R. J. and Hu, W. (2008) A blend of essential plant oils used as an additive to alter silage fermentation or used as a feed additive for lactating dairy cows. *Journal of Dairy Science*, **91**, 4793–4800

Lourenço, M., Vlaeminck, B., Van Ranst, G., De Smet, S. and Fievez, V. (2007c) Influence of different dietary forages on the fatty acid composition of rumen digesta and ruminant meat and milk. *Animal Feed Science and Technology*, **145**, 418-437.

Lourenço, M., Vlaeminck, B., Bruinenberg, M., Demeyer, D. and Fievez, V. (2005) Milk fatty acid composition and associated rumen lipolysis and fatty acid hydrogenation when feeding forages from intensively managed or semi-natural grasslands. *Animal Research*, **54**, 471-484.

Lourenço, M., Van Ranst, G., De Smet, S., Raes, K. and Fievez, V. (2007b) Effect of grazing pastures with different botanical composition by lambs on rumen fatty acid metabolism and fatty acid pattern of Longissimus muscle 424 and subcutaneous fat. *Animal*, **1**, 537-545.

Lourenço, M., De Smet, S., Raes, K. and Fievez, V. (2007a) Effect of botanical composition of silages on rumen fatty acid metabolism and fatty aicd comosition in Logissimus muscle and subcutaneous fat of lambs. *Animal*, **1**, 911-921.

Marino, M., Bersani, C. and Comi, G. (2001) Impedance measurements to study the antimicrobial activity of essential oils from Lamiacea and Compositae. *International Journal of Food Microbiology*, **67**, 187– 195.

Martin, S.A. and Macy, J.M. (1985) Effects of monensin, pyromellitic diimide and 2-bromoethanesulfonic acid on rumen fermentation *in vitro. Journal of Animal Science*, **60**, 544-550.

McIntosh, F. M., Newbold, C. J., Losa, R., Williams, P. and Wallace, R.J. (2000) Effects of essential oils on rumen fermentation. *Reproduction Nutrition Development*, **40**, 221-222.

McIntosh, F. M., Williams, P., Losa, R., Wallace, R.J., Beever, D.A. and Newbold, C.J. (2003) Effects of essential oils on ruminal microorganisms and their protein metabolism. *Applied and Environmental Microbiology*, **69**, 5011-5014.

Meyer, N.F., Erickson, G.E., Klopfenstein, T.J., Greenquist, M.A., Luebbe, M.K., Williams, P., and Engstrom, M.A. (2009) Effect of essential oils, tylosin, and monensin on finishing steer performance, carcass characteristics, liver abscesses, ruminal fermentation, and digestibility. *Journal of Animalence*, **87**(7), 2346-54.

Miller, T. L., and Wollin., M.J. (2001) Inhibition of growth of methane-producing bacteria of the ruminant forestomach by Hydroxymethylglutaryl-SCoA reductase inhibitors. *Journal of Dairy Science*, **84**, 1445-1448.

Molero, R., Ibars, M., Calsamiglia, S., Ferret, A. and Losa, R. (2004) Effect of a specific blend of essential oil compounds on dry matter and crude protein degradability in heifers fed diets with different forage to concentrate rations. *Animal Feed Science and Technology*, **114**, 91-104.

Nagy, J. G., and R. P. Tengerdy,. R.P. (1968). Antibacterial action of essential oils of Artemisia as an ecological factor. II. Antibacterial action of the volatile oils of Artemisia tridentata (Big Sagebrush) on bacteria from the rumen of mule deer. *Applied Microbiology*, **16**, 441-444.

Newbold, C. J., McIntosch, F.M., Williams, P., Losa, R. and Wallace, R.J. (2004) Effects of a specific blend of essential oil compounds on rumen fermentation. *Animal Feed Science and Technology*, **114**, 105-112.

Nombekela S.W., Murphy, M.R., Gonyou, H.W. and Marden, J.I. (1994) Dietary preferences in early lactation cows as affected by primary tastes and some common feed flavors. *Journal of Dairy Science*, **77**, 2393-2399.

Oh, H. K., Jones, M.B. and Longhurst,. W.M. (1968) Comparison of rumen microbial inhibition resulting from various essential oils isolated from relatively unpalatable plant species. *Applied Microbiology*, **16**, 39-44.

Oh,. J., Hristov, A.N., Lee, C., Cassidy, T., Heyler, K., Varga, G.A., Pate, J., Walusimbi, S., Brzezicka, E., Toyokawa, K., Werner, J., Donkin, S.S., Elias, R., Dowd, S. and, Bravo, D. (2013) Immune and production responses of dairy cows to postruminal supplementation with phytonutrients. *Journal of Dairy Science*, **96**, 7830-43.

Prescott, L. M., Harley, J.P. and Klein,. D.A. (2004) Control de microorganismos por agentes físicos y químicos. In: *Microbiología*. Mc Graw-Hill-Interamericana de España, ed. Madrid, Spain. pp 145-162

Rodríguez-Prado, M., Ferret, A., Zwieten, J., González, L., Bravo, D. and, Calsamiglia, S., (2012) Effects of dietary addition of capsicum extracto n intake, wáter consumption, and rumen fermentation of fattening heifers fed a high-concentrate diet. J. Anim. Sci.Journal of Animal Science, 90:, 1879-1884.

Santos, F.H., De Paula, M.R., Lezier, D. Silva, J.T., Santos, G. and Bittar, C.M. (2015) .Essential oils for dairy calves: effects on performance, scours, rumen fermentation and intestinal fauna. Animal. 9(6):, 958-65.

Santos, M.B., Robinson, P.H., Williams, P. and Losa, R. (2010.) Effects of addition of an essential oil complexto the diet of lactating dairy cows on whole tract digestion of nutrients and productive performance. Animal Feed Science and Technology, 157:, 64–71

Sivropoulou, A., E. Papanikolau, E., C. Nikolau, C., S. Kokkini, S., T. Lanaras, T. and M. Arsenakis,. M. (1996). Antimicrobial and cytotoxic activities of Origanum essential oils. J. Agric. Food ChemJournal of Agricultural and Food Chemistry., 44:, 1202-1205.

Spanghero, M., Robinson, P.H., Zanfi, C. and, Fabbro, E. (2009). Effect of increasing doses of a microencapsulated blend of essential oils on performance of lactating primiparous dairy cows. Animal Feed Science and Technology, 153:, 153-157.

Tager, L. R. and Krause, K. M. (2011.) Effects of essential oils on rumen fermentation, milk production, and feeding behavior in lactating dairy cows. J. Dairy Sci.Journal of Dairy Science, 94:, 2455–2464

Tamminga, S. (1996). A review on environmental impacts of nutritional strategies in ruminants. J. Anim. Sci.Journal of Animal Science, 74:, 3112-3124.

Tassou, C.C.,, E.H. Drosinos, E.H. and G.J.E. Nychas,. G.J.E. (1995). Effects of essential oil from mint (Mentha piperita) on Salmonella enteritidis and Listeria monocytogenes in model food systems at 4° and 10°C. J. Appl. BactJournal of Applied Bacteriology. 78: 78:, 593–600

Tekippe , J. A., Tacoma, R. Hristov, A. N. Lee, C., Oh, J., Heyler, K. S. Cassidy, T. W. Varga, G. A. and Bravo, D. (2013). Effect of essential oils on ruminal fermentation and lactation performance of dairy cows. J. Dairy Sci.Journal of Dairy Science, 96:, 7892–7903

Tekippe, J. A., Hristov, A. N., Heyler, K. S., Cassidy, T. W., Zheljazkov, V. D., Ferreira, J. F. S., Karnati, S. K., and Varga, G. A. (2011.) Rumen fermentation and production effects of Origanum vulgare L. leaves in lactating dairy cows. J. Dairy Sci.Journal of Dairy Science, 94:, 5065–5079

Ultee, A., E.P. Kets, E.P. and E. J. Smid., E.J. (1999). Mechanisms of action of carvacrol on the food-borne pathogen Bacillus cereus. Appl. Environ. MicrobiolApplied and Environmental Applied Microbiology., 65:, 4606-4610.

Ultee, A., M. H. J. Bennik, M.H.J. and R. Moezelaar,. R. (2002). The phenolic hydroxyl group of carvacrol is essential for action against the food-borne pathogen Bacillus cereus. Applied and Environmental Applied Microbiology, Appl. Environ. Microbiol. 68:, 1561-1568.

Vakili A.R., Khorrami B., Danesh Mesgaran M. and, Parand, E., (2013). The effects of thyme and cinnamon essential oils on performance, rumen fermentation and blood metabolites in Holstein calves consuming high concentrate diet. Asian Australas. J. Anim. Sci.Journal of Animal Science, 26:, 935-944.

Wall, E.H., Doane, P.H., Donkin, S.S., and Bravo, D. (2014). The effects of supplementation with a blend of cinnamaldehyde and eugenol on feed intake and milk production of dairy cows. *Journal of Dairy Science*, **97**, 5709–5717.

Wallace, R.J. and Cotta, M.A. (1988) Metabolism of nitrogen containing compounds. In: *The Rumen Microbial Echosystem*. Edited by P.N. Hobson. Elsevier Applied Sciences. London.

Wallace, R. J., McEwan, N.R., McIntosh, F.M., Teferedegne, B. and Newbold, C.J. (2002) Natural products as manipulators of rumen fermentation. Asian-Austr. *Journal of Animal Science*, **10**, 1458-1468.

Wanapat, M., Cherdthong, A., Pakdee, P. and, Wanapat, S. (2008) Manipulation of rumen ecology by dietary lemongrass (Cymbopogon citratus Stapf.) powder supplementation. *Journal of Animal Science*, **86**(12):, 3497-503.

Weller, R.F. and Phipps, R.H. (1989.) Preliminary studies on the effect of flavouring agents on the dry-matter intake of silage by lactating dairy cows. *Journal of Agricultural Science*, **112**:, 67-71

Wendakoon, C. N., and Sakaguchi, M. (1995) Inhibition of amino acid decarboxylase activity of Enterobacter aerogenes by active components in spices. *Journal of Food Protection*, **58**, 280-283.

Yang, W. Z., Benchaar, C., Ametaj, B. N. and, Beauchemin, K. A., (2010b) Dose response to eugenol supplementation in growing beef cattle: Ruminal fermentation and intestinal digestion. *Animal Feed Science and Technology*, **158**, 57-64.

Yang, W. Z., Ametaj, B. N., Benchaar, C., He, M. L. and, Beauchemin, K. A., (2010a) Cinnamaldehyde in feedlot cattle diets: Intake, growth performance, carcass characteristics, and blood metabolites. *Journal of Animal Science*, **88**, 1082-1092.

Yang, W.Z. Benchaar, C. Ametaj, B.N. and Beauchemin, K.A. (2010) cDose response to eugenol supplementation in growing beef cattle: Ruminal fermentation and intestinal digestion, *Animal Feed Science and Technology*, **158**(1–2), 57-64.

Yang, W.Z., Ametaj, B.N., Benchaar, C. and, Beauchemin, K.A. (2010a) Dose response to cinnamaldehyde supplementation in growing beef heifers: ruminal and intestinal digestion. *Journal of Animal Science*, **88**(2), 680-688.

Yang, W.Z., Benchaar, C., Ametaj, B.N., Chaves, A.V., He, M.L. and McAllister, T.A. (2007) Effects of garlic and juniper berry essential oils on ruminal fermentation and on the site and extent of digestion in lactating cows. *Journal of Dairy Science*, **90**, 5671–5681.

6

The Rumen Microbiome : Future Prospects And Applications In Animal Nutrition

R.J. WALLACE, T.J. SNELLING AND C.A. MCCARTNEY

Rowett Institute of Nutrition and Health, University of Aberdeen, Bucksburn AB32 6YF, UK

Introduction

The technology that most people associate with –omics technologies is the DNA sequencing instrumentation that now enables a human genome to be sequenced in a matter of hours at a cost that approaches $1000. This compares with the first human genome project, which cost in the region of $10 billion and took 10 years to achieve. Such sequencing power, which derives in large part from development of laser and fluorophore technology, enables us to contemplate undertaking as a common procedure the sequencing of all DNA present in a complex microbial ecosystem such as the rumen, and to compare different samples readily using computer power that has advanced out of recognition at the same time. The aim of this paper is to point the way forward to practical outcomes of this transformation in microbiological capability.

Microbiota, metagenomics, microbiomes

We seem to hear daily new words ending in '-omics' or '-ome', the former referring to the technology, the latter to the results that are generated by the particular '-omics' technology. Many of the new words are spurious, because they refer to old technologies finding a new, catchy name, but others refer to fantastic advances in technology that have transformed our understanding of biology. The first of the new words was 'genomics', which involved using new sequencing technologies and softwares that enabled us to understand the structure of microbial, plant and animal genomes – single organisms. Subsequently, more advanced technologies and computer programmes were developed to describe ecosystems that were inhabited by large numbers of different species, leading to new terms like microbiota, metagenome and the word in the title, microbiome. Some explanation may be needed to clarify what these words mean.

'Microbiota' is the least ambiguous of the words. It means the sum of all microbial species and their abundance in a complex ecosystem. It refers to eukaryotic microorganisms like protozoa and fungi as well as the prokaryotic bacteria and archaea. Determining the composition of the microbiota is, or taxonomic analysis is, almost always derived from small-subunit ribosomal RNA (ss rRNA) gene sequence analysis. The three dimensional structure of the single-stranded ss rRNA (18S rRNA for eukaryotes, 16S rRNA for prokaryotes) is determined by regions in which nucleotides hydrogen-bond with each other, forming base pairs. These nucleotides have been conserved throughout evolution much more than in the other, variable regions (Figure 1). The differences between two organisms in sequence within the variable regions can give an impression of how long ago they diverged from each other. It is also from these variable regions that the taxonomic identity can be derived. Almost all microbiologists would agree with this definition of microbiota. Robert Herd of Armidale, New South Wales, in an aptly Australian way, described it to RJW as "who's who in the zoo", a memorable description.

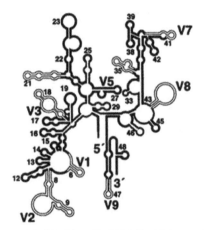

Figure 1. Secondary-Structure Model of the 16S rDNA (double lines indicate variable or hypervariable; gray lines indicate highly conserved; V1 to V9 indicate major variable regions). From Tortoli (2003) Clin. Microbiol. Rev. 16:319-354.

Much less agreement would be reached among microbiologists on the meanings of metagenome and microbiome, particularly the latter. For the present authors, the metagenome just means the totality of genes that are present in the microbiota, obtained by sequencing extracted DNA, without any taxonomic assignment, while the microbiome also has connotations of the taxonomic origin of the genes. A recent paper by Whiteside *et al.* (2015) came up with similar definitions of microbiota and metagenome to those described above, but a completely different definition of microbiome, including in its definition the chemical environment. Internet searches reveal many other definitions of microbiome and metagenome, each with slightly different emphasis. Microbiome seems likely, as technology develops, to revert to the definition of Yang (2012) as 'the collective genomes present in an ecological niche'. Nonetheless, as even those researchers directly involved in the field cannot agree, it serves us best to ignore the niceties and just think of microbiota as who's there and the others as what genes are there.

An example of the information that can be derived from deep-sequencing rumen microbial DNA

Although not the first paper that described rumen metagenomics analysis, the report in Science by Hess *et al.* (2011) illustrates very nicely what sort of useful biological information may be derived from metagenomics analysis. By comparing the microbiota adhering to switchgrass suspended in the rumen with the microbiota present in the rest of the digesta, Hess *et al.* (2011) hoped to identify organisms that were enriched on the switchgrass. The extraction of ss rRNA sequences from the whole metagenomes enabled them to be compared with similar sequences appearing in public databases, thereby identifying the most abundant members of the microbiota in both niches. It emerged that at least five operational taxonomic units (OTU, equivalent to bacterial species) were enriched on the switchgrass (Figure 2). None of these was from a cultivated species, indicating a major opportunity to isolate the enriched species that by implication could be involved in switchgrass degradation and therefore be useful in the biofuels industry.

Hess *et al.* (2011) also used their metagenome sequences to carry out some enzyme mining. There are different ways of doing this. One involves the strategy employed by Hess *et al.*, namely to screen the whole set of sequences for genes with sequence similarity to known genes that encode the desired activity. The CAZy database holds sequence information on known glycosyl hydrolases, from the rumen and elsewhere. Hess *et al.* (2011) searched for new genes in their metagenome, finding 25,947 candidate genes, then expressed 90 of the enzymes and tested their activities. The other main strategy for gene mining is to make a clone library and to test for the desired activity. Although much more laborious, this strategy has a greater chance of discovering previously unknown types of activity. Examples include successful searches for glycosyl hydrolases (Ferrer *et al.* 2005; Bao *et al.* 2012; Ko *et al.* 2013; Rashamuse *et al.* 2013; Patel *et al.* 2016), polyphenol oxidases (Beloqui *et al.* 2006), and lipases (Liu *et al.* 2009; Privé *et al.* 2012).

One of the most amazing capabilities that can be derived from metagenomes is that entire genomes of bacteria can be constructed from the data, even if the bacteria has never been isolated and grown in pure culture before. Hess *et al.* (2011) constructed

15 of these genomes, all of which were from uncultivated species. Pope *et al.* (2011) achieved a remarkable corollary, when they identified an important new species by constructing its genome from the metagenome of the wallaby, predicting the metabolic capability of the new species from its genome, then designed a growth medium for its selective growth. The isolated bacteria were identical to that predicted from the metagenome.

Other information that has been extracted from the rumen metagenome is the incidence of antibiotic resistance genes (Singh *et al.* 2012), CRISPR elements (Berg Miller *et al.* 2011), and the main metabolic pathways that the microbiota use. The last of these will be illustrated below in the context of methane emissions.

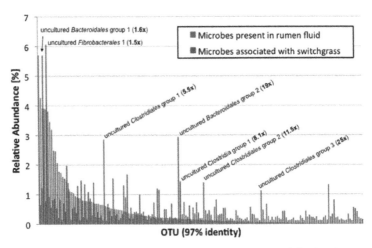

Figure 2. Rank abundance profiles of bacterial abundance in ruminal fluid and on switchgrass suspended in the rumen. The seven phylotypes (equivalent to species) highlighted differ markedly in abundance, suggesting an important role in the breakdown of switchgrass. All are so far uncultured. The information was obtained from the abundance of 16S rRNA gene sequences.

Methane emissions

Methane is a greenhouse gas with a global warming potential 28-fold that of carbon dioxide. Ruminant livestock production, through the fermentation of feed in the gut, contributes significantly to greenhouse gas production by agriculture. In the UK in 2005, CH4 accounted for 37% of all agricultural emissions. Methane production also represents a loss of energy (from 2 to 12% of gross energy intake: Johnson & Johnson, 1995), which would otherwise be available for growth or milk production. Lowering methane emissions therefore would benefit the environment and the efficiency of livestock production. More than 95% of the methane produced by cattle is derived from the rumen, where a population of methanogenic archaea converts the H_2 and CO_2 produced by a complex community of ciliate protozoa, bacteria and anaerobic fungi to methane (Martin *et al.*, 2010). A massive worldwide research effort has investigated various mitigation strategies, particularly feed additives that might inhibit H_2 production, provide an alternative H sink or inhibit the archaea themselves. Other strategies include chemogenomics, and immunization (Attwood *et al.*, 2011). A strategy that could be most sustainable is genetic selection for low methane-emitting animals. If we can demonstrate that the different volumes of methane emissions in different animals can be explained by their differing ruminal microbiomes, and that the property is persistent and heritable, it should be possible to select future generations of cattle and sheep that have intrinsically lower methane emissions. Lower methane emissions would also be expected to improve the efficiency of energy retention and thereby increase feed efficiency.

Methane emissions are difficult to measure in large numbers of animals suitable for genetic analysis. Geneticists (de Haas *et al.* 2011) have showed that, theoretically, lower methane emissions can be achieved through selection on associated traits, such as residual feed intake (RFI) or through selection on methane predicted from feed intake and diet composition. Experimental data were used from 548 heifers. RFI is the difference between net energy intake and calculated net energy requirements for maintenance as a function of body weight and for fat- and protein-corrected milk production. Predicted methane emission (PME) was calculated as 6% of gross energy intake (Intergovernmental Panel on Climate Change methodology). The estimated heritabilities for PME and RFI were 0.35 and 0.40, respectively. The positive genetic correlation between RFI and PME indicated that cows with lower RFI have lower PME (estimates ranging from 0.18 to 0.84). It was concluded that it is possible to decrease the methane production of a cow by selecting more-efficient cows. The genetic variation suggested that reductions in the order of 11 to 26% in 10 years are theoretically possible.

Goopy *et al.* (2006) reported that divergent methane emissions in different steers persisted over periods of 1-3 months. Differences in the proportions of fermentation products and on the protozoal population also persisted, with the implication that the animal itself played a major role in determining its ruminal microbiome and consequently its metabolic activity.

Together with collaborators at SRUC and the Roslin Institute, Edinburgh, Rowett researchers have established that the abundance of archaea in the rumen of steers at slaughter parallels that measured when the animal was alive (Wallace *et al.*, 2014). Furthermore, we have demonstrated that progeny from some sires have higher methane emissions than those from other sires, indicating a host-animal genetic component to methane emissions (Duthie *et al.* 2013). But most information has been obtained from studying metagenomics sequencing, identifying members of the microbiota and their genes that are key to determining methane emissions.

The ruminal microbiota in steers with contrasting methane emissions were compared. 16S rRNA gene abundances indicated that archaea, predominantly Methanobrevibacter, were 2.5× more numerous in high emitters, whereas among bacteria Proteobacteria, predominantly Succinivibrionaceae, were less abundant in high emitters (2.7%) than in low emitters (11.2%). This observation has a curious correspondence with the abundance of Succinivibrionaceae in the digestive tract of the Tammar wallaby (9% of total bacteria) (Pope *et al.* 2010), which was considered to be the main reason why the Tammar wallaby produces one quarter of the methane emissions of cattle (Pope *et al.* 2010, 2011). Succinivibrionaceae were just as abundant in the low-emission beef cattle as in the wallaby. These bacteria produce succinate as a main fermentation product, thus trapping metabolic hydrogen rather than releasing it as H_2 The finding that Succinivibrionaceae were much more numerous in low-emitting cows is consistent with the wallaby observations and offers a possible strategy – enriching for these bacteria - for lower methane emissions from ruminant livestock.

In the same study, the abundance of genes in the metagenomes was compared between the low and high emitters. Various softwares and databases can be used for this purpose, the most commonly used being KEGG (Kyoto Encyclopedia of Genes and Genomes). Thus, the position of the various genes in metabolic pathways can be identified, such as those genes related to methane formation (Figure 3). Comparisons between the low and high emitting cattle revealed that archaeal genes leading directly or indirectly to methane production were 2.7-fold more abundant in high emitters (Wallace *et al.* 2015). Genes less abundant in high emitters included acetate kinase, electron transport complex proteins RnfC and RnfD and glucose-6-phosphate isomerase. From the geneticist's viewpoint, the relative abundance of the microbial enzyme genes to predict methane emissions with 20 genes explained 87% of its variation. These results open up the implementation of cost-effective breeding strategies for difficult to measure traits such as methane emissions and feed efficiency based on the abundance of microbial enzyme genes.

Sub-acute ruminal acidosis

Sub-acute ruminal acidosis (SARA) is a disorder that can afflict all ruminant species, but one that is particularly prevalent in intensively produced dairy and beef cattle (Thomas 2004). It results from dysfunction of ruminal microbial ecology. SARA is associated with reduced fibre degradation, reduced feed intake, laminitis and diarrhoea and thereby also increased involuntary culling. Its economic impact is therefore highly significant.

When forage comprises the predominant proportion of the ruminant's diet, the rumen is extremely robust and resilient, and management changes have little adverse

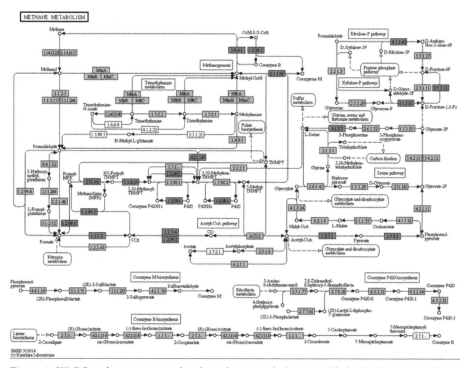

Figure 3. KEGG pathways associated with methane metabolism. Highlighted EC gene numbers are those genes that differed significantly between high and low emitting cattle. Red – genes that had higher abundance in high emitters; yellow - gene that had lower abundance in high emitters. From Wallace *et al.* (2015).

impact on efficiency or health. This changes, however, as we intensify production systems and rely less on forage and more on cereals and purchased concentrates. Starch is fermented quickly, leading to rapid production of fermentation acids. Usually fermentation acids (acetate, propionate and butyrate mainly) are absorbed across the rumen wall, providing energy nutrients to the host animal, and a moderate concentration remains in the ruminal digestion mixture. The large amounts of saliva formed by ruminants serve to buffer the acidic properties of these microbial products, but it is not a very efficient system. When the pH-control system is overwhelmed, 'acidosis' occurs and problems associated with the resultant changes in microbial ecology become prevalent. There is a catastrophic form of acidosis that causes virtually all of the ruminal microbiota to die, leaving only acid-tolerant Lactobacillus species to flourish (Slyter 1976). Large concentrations of lactic acid are produced. The acidity-control mechanism is so overwhelmed that the animal can die within a day. The condition always results from a too rapid intake of starchy diet. The acute form of the disease is relatively rare in the UK, however, and the acidosis that we see most often is a less catastrophic form, but one that nevertheless causes distress and loss of productivity, namely SARA.

SARA combines several effects, each of which is detrimental to animal production. The most evident at post mortem is inflammation of the rumen wall, leading to abrasion and malformation of papillae in some animals (Figure 5). The precise cause of SARA has long been a subject of debate. An excellent example of microbiological detective work in trying to elucidate the primary cause has been conducted at the University of Manitoba, in which a 'microbiome' analysis played a significant part (Khafipour *et al.* 2009a). In fact, by our earlier definitions, this was a microbiota analysis based on 16S rRNA analysis, and the microbiota analysis was conducted by qPCR of 16S rRNA from known target microbial species rather than by untargeted shotgun sequencing. Two models of experimentally induced SARA were used, one grain-induced, the other alfalfa-induced. The microbiota analysis showed that changes in microbiota taxonomy were different for the different induction methods (Figure 6), with increased Escherichia coli abundance being implicated in the grain-induced condition (Khafipour *et al.* 2009a). This finding was consistent with the group's previous finding that soluble lipopolysaccharide (LPS) with endotoxin activity, which *E. coli* produces more than other bacterial species, correlated with the severity of SARA (Khafipour *et al.* 2009b). The same group followed up by identifying which strains, with characteristic virulence factors, were key to the pathology (Khafipour *et al.* 2011).

The SARA story is not that simple, however. The severity of SARA varies across different herds, even on apparently similar diets, and varies among different animals within herds. Although this is a problem for producers, it potentially offers an opportunity for researchers to find ways of replicating conditions in SARA-tolerant animals across the herd, possibly by adding live microbial feed additives that suppress growth of *E. coli*, or others that bind the soluble LPS or adhere directly to Gram-negative bacteria.

Conclusion

Although the outcomes of analyses enabled by rapid DNA sequencing are frequently highly academic in nature, the examples provided here indicate that there is great potential for useful outcomes for animal productivity and health. Feed conversion efficiency, efficiency of N retention, resistance to bloat and other aspects of ruminal metabolism and ruminant production are other targets where microbiota/metagenome/microbiome research can provide answers to long-standing issues in ruminant livestock production.

Figure 4. Healthy (left) and damaged (right) rumen wall papillae. Papillae damage seen in the photograph on the right is typical of SARA

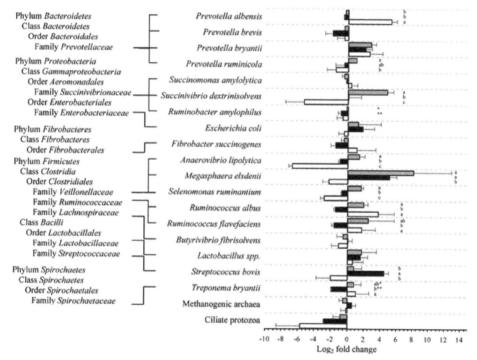

Figure 5. Changes (log10) in predominant ruminal bacteria, as determined by 16S rRNA gene abundance in mild (grey bars) and severe (black bars) grain-induced acidosis and alfalfa-induced acidosis. From Khafipour *et al.* (2009a)

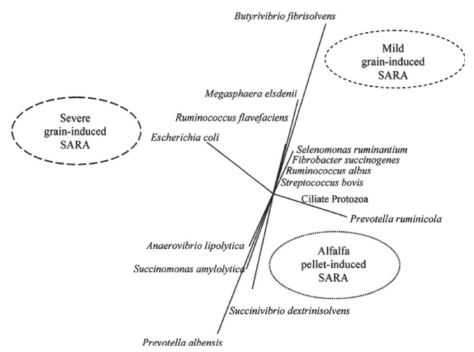

Figure 6. Discriminant analysis of predominant ruminal bacteria in response to induced SARA. From Khafipour *et al.* (2009a)

Acknowledgements

The Rowett Institute of Nutrition and Health is funded by the Rural and Environment Science and Analytical Services Division (RESAS) of the Scottish Government. This work was supported by RuminOmics and funded by the European Commission (Grant Agreement No. 289319), also by the Biotechnology and Biological Research Council, UK (Industrial Partnership Award BB/J016608/1).

References

Attwood, G.T., Altermann, E., Kelly, W.J., Leahy, S.C., Zhang, L. and Morrison, M. (2011) Exploring rumen methanogen genomes to identify targets for methane mitigation strategies. *Animal Feed Science and Technology*, **166-67**, 65-75.

Bao, L., Huang, Q., Chang, L., Sun, Q., Zhou, J. and Lu, H. (2012) Cloning and characterization of two beta-glucosidase/xylosidase enzymes from yak rumen metagenome. *Applied Biochemistry and Biotechnology*, **166**, 72-86.

Beloqui, A., Pita, M., Polaina, J., Martínez, A., Golyshina, O.V., Zumárraga, M., Yakimov, M.M., García-Arellano, H., Alcalde, M., Fernández, V.M., Elborough, K., Andreu, J.M., Ballesteros, A., Plou, F.J., Timmis, K.N., Ferrer, M. and, Golyshin, P.N. (2006)

Novel polyphenol oxidase mined from a metagenome expression library of bovine rumen - biochemical properties, structural analysis, and phylogenetic relationships. *Journal of Biological Chemistry*, **281**, 22933-22942.

de Haas, Y., Windig, J.J., Calus, M.P.L., Dijkstra, J., de Haan, M., Bannink, A. and Veerkamp, R.F. (2011) Genetic parameters for predicted methane production and potential for reducing enteric emissions through genomic selection. *Journal of Dairy Science*, **94**, 6122-6134.

Duthie, C-A., Rooke, J.A., Hyslop, J.J., Ross, D.W. and Waterhouse, A. (2013) Methane emissions of two divergent breeds of beef suckler cows offered a straw based diet with either grass silage or brewers grains. *Advances in Animal Biosciences: Proceedings of the 5th Greenhouse Gases and Animal Agriculture Conference* (GGAA 2013), Dublin, Ireland. Cambridge University Press, Vol. 4 (2), p. 575.

Ferrer, M., Golyshina, O.V., Chernikova, T.N., Khachane, A.N., Martins dos Santos, V.A.P., Strompl, C., Yakimov, M.M., Elborough, K., Jarvis, G., Neef, A., Timmis, K.N. and Golyshin, P.N. (2005) Novel hydrolase diversity retrieved from a metagenome library of bovine rumen microflora. *Environmental Microbiology*, **7**, 1996-2010.

Goopy, J. P., Hegarty, R.S. and Dobos, R.C. (2006) The persistence over time of divergent methane production in lot fed cattle. *International Congress Series* **1293**, 111-114.

Hess, M., Sczyrba, A., Egan, R., Kim, T.W., Chokhawala, H., Schroth, G., Luo, S.J., Clark, D.S., Chen, F., Zhang, T., Mackie, R.I., Pennacchio, L.A., Tringe, S.G., Visel, A., Woyke, T., Wang, Z. and Rubin, E.M. (2011) Metagenomic discovery of biomass-degrading genes and genomes from cow rumen. *Science*, **331**, 463-467.

Johnson, K.A. and Johnson, D. E. (1995) Methane emissions from cattle. *Journal of Animal Science*, **73**, 2483-2492.

Martin, C., Morgavi, D.P., and Doreau, M. (2010) Methane mitigation in ruminants: from microbe to the farm scale. *Animal*, **4**, 351-365.

Muth, T., Benndorf, D., Reichl, U., Rapp, E. and Martens, L. (2013) Searching for a needle in a stack of needles: challenges in metaproteomics data analysis. *Molecular BioSystems*, **9**, 578-585.

Khafipour, E., Li, S.C., Plaizier, J.C. and Krause, D.O. (2009a) Rumen microbiome composition determined using two nutritional models of subacute ruminal acidosis. *Applied and Environmental Microbiology*, **75**, 7115-7124.

Khafipour, E., Krause, D.O. and Plaizier, J.C. (2009b) A grain-based subacute ruminal acidosis challenge causes translocation of lipopolysaccharide and triggers inflammation. *Journal of Dairy Science*, **92**, 1060-1070.

Khafipour, E., Plaizier, J.C., Aikman, P.C. and Krause, D.O. (2011) Population structure of rumen Escherichia coli associated with subacute ruminal acidosis (SARA) in dairy cattle. *Journal of Dairy Science*, **94**, 351-360.

Ko, K.C., Lee, J.H., Han, Y., Choi, J.H. and Song, J.J. (2013) A novel multifunctional cellulolytic enzyme screened from metagenomic resources representing ruminal bacteria. *Biochemical and Biophysical Research Communications*, **441**, 567-572.

Liu, K., Wang, J., Bu, D., Zhao, S., McSweeney, C., Yu, P. and Li, D. (2009) Isolation and biochemical characterization of two lipases from a metagenomic library of China Holstein cow rumen. *Biochemical and Biophysical Research Communications*, **385**, 605-611.

Patel, A.B., Patel, A.K., Shah, M.P., Parikh, I.K. and Joshi, C.G. (2016) Isolation and characterization of novel multifunctional recombinant family 26 glycoside hydrolase from mehsani buffalo rumen metagenome. *Biotechnology and Applied Biochemistry*, **63(2)**, 257-265.

Pope, P.B., Denman, S.E., Jones, M., Tringe, S.G., Barry, K., Malfatti, S.A., McHardy, A.C., Cheng, J.F., Hugenholtz, P., McSweeney, C.S. and Morrison, M. (2010) Adaptation to herbivory by the Tammar wallaby includes bacterial and glycoside hydrolase profiles different from other herbivores. *Proceedings of the National Academy of Science USA*, **107**, 14793-14798.

Pope, P.B., Smith, W., Denman, S.E., Tringe, S.G., Barry, K., Hugenholtz, P., McSweeney, C.S., McHardy, A.C. and Morrison, M. (2011) Isolation of Succinivibrionaceae Implicated in Low Methane Emissions from Tammar Wallabies. *Science*, **333**, 646-648.

Privé, F., Newbold, C.J., Kaderbhai, N.N., Girdwood, S.G., Golyshina, O.V., Golyshin, P.N., Scollan, N.D. and Huws, S.A. (2015) Isolation and characterization of novel lipases/esterases from a bovine rumen metagenome. *Applied Microbiology and Technology*, **99(13)**, 5475-5485.

Rashamuse, K. J., Visser, D.F., Hennessy, F., Kemp, J., Roux-van der Merwe, M.P., Badenhorst, J., Ronneburg, T., Francis-Pope, R. and Brady, D. (2013) Characterisation of two bifunctional cellulase-xylanase enzymes isolated from a bovine rumen metagenome library. *Current Microbiology*, **66**, 145-151.

Singh, K.M., Jakhesara, S.J., Koringa, P.G., Rank, D.N. and Joshi, C.G. (2012) Metagenomic analysis of virulence-associated and antibiotic resistance genes of microbes in rumen of Indian buffalo (Bubalus bubalis). *Gene*, **507**, 146-151.

Slyter, L. L. (1976) Influence of acidosis on rumen function. *Journal of Animal Science*, **43**, 910-929.

Thomas, C. (2004) Sub-acute ruminal acidosis: a major challenge facing UK farmers. *Feed Compounder*. February, 20-22.

Wallace, R. J., Rooke, J.A., Duthie, C.A., Hyslop, J.J., Ross, D.W., McKain, N., de Souza, S.M., Snelling, T.J., Waterhouse, A. and Roehe, R. (2014) Archaeal abundance in post-mortem ruminal digesta may help predict methane emissions from beef cattle. *Scientific Reports*, **4**, 5892.

Wallace, R.J., Rooke, J.A., McKain, N., Duthie, C.A., Hyslop, J.J., Ross, D.W., Waterhouse, A., Watson, M. and Roeh, R. (2015) The rumen microbial metagenome associated with high methane production in cattle. *BMC Genomics*, **16**, 839.

Whiteside, S.A., Razvi, H., Dave, S., Reid, G. and Burton, J.P. (2015) The microbiome of the urinary tract--a role beyond infection. *Nature Reviews Urology*, **12**, 81-90.

Yang, J. (2102). The Human Microbiome Project: Extending the definition of what constitutes a human. www.genome.gov/27549400.

7

7

THE GUT MICROBIOME: PROSPECTS FOR ANIMAL HEALTH

M.J. WOODWARD

Department of Food and Nutritional Sciences, The University of Reading, PO Box 226, Whiteknights, Reading RG6 6AP

Introduction

The microbial population of the gut (microbiota) in mammals is very complex, comprising hundreds to thousands of species of bacteria, viruses, fungi and protozoa reflecting the nutrition of mammals and the different regions and functionalities of the gut. The microbiota contributes to mammalian health by processing complex substrates that the host cannot readily digest and generating metabolites such as vitamins, aromatic amino acids and short chain fatty acids essential for host metabolism. Surprisingly, the gut is considered as 'external' to the mammalian host being part of the environment with the gut epithelium being the barrier and a major immunological response organ preventing infections. A mature microbiota is known to suppress pathogens, the Nurmi effect, and much emphasis in human and animal health is placed upon developing and recovering a stable mature gut microbiota after so-called gut 'dysbacteriosis' caused by nutritional shifts, antibiotic treatment, stress and ageing.

This chapter provides a brief overview of how current genetic methodologies of next generation sequencing (NGS) are used to describe bacterial populations of the microbiota and to define the entire genetic content of the microbiota, true metagenomics. In addition, one of the main tools for analysing the metabolic impact of the microbiota on the luminal content of the gut and the metabolites that enter the host, namely nuclear magnetic resonance (NMR), is discussed briefly.

Feed conversion and meat to carcass weight ratios are key measures of the impact on productivity. These are influenced by the diet, but until recently diet formulation has only taken into account gross parameters of production as the measure of success. With the ability to interrogate the gut microbiota it may be argued that such measures can be refined by assessing both the gut microbiota and its impact on the host metabolome. For example, recent studies show associations between certain members of the gut microbiota and weight gain and loss in model systems.

So, an often asked question is, over and above basic nutritional dietary balance, can other manipulations improve animal health and productivity? This chapter also discusses the possibilities for diet supplementation with probiotics, prebiotics, phytochemicals along with conventional treatments such as vaccination and antibiotic used in animal husbandry with a focus on interactions between the gut microbiota and gastro-intestinal and food-borne zoonotic diseases in particular. Although the principles apply to all animal species, this chapter uses pigs and poultry as its primary exemplar animal hosts.

A brief overview of the gut microbiota and its many roles

The microbial population of the gut (microbiota) in animals is very complex and its diversity broad, comprising bacteria, viruses, fungi and protozoa. The microbial diversity will also reflect the nutritional types of animals, the diet and the different functionalities of each region and of the gut. For avian and non-ruminant animals, the distal region of the gut, the large bowel and caecum, have the largest number of bacteria and where most microbial fermentation takes place. There are various estimates of the numbers of different bacterial species present here, varying from hundreds to thousands. Until recently, a major limitation of their analysis has been the dependency upon traditional cultural methods to grow isolates in the laboratory. However, today this has been revolutionised by molecular non-cultural methods which will be discussed later.

There is a suggested concept of the gut with its host acting as a 'super-organism' (Lederberg, 2000; Gill *et al.*, 2006; Spor *et al.*, 2011). The microbiota contributes to health by processing complex substrates that the host cannot readily digest such as non-digestible fibres and generating metabolites such as vitamins, aromatic amino acids and short chain fatty acids, notably butyrate, essential for host metabolism. As seen in studies comparing gnotobiotic (bacteria free) and conventional animals, whether mouse, chick or piglet, the gut microbiota has a profound effect on digestion and rate of growth (Muramatsu *et al.*, 1991; Muramatsu *et al.*, 1994). Indeed, without a mature gut flora growth is severely limited. Other than nutritional benefits to the host, gut microbiota also provides two very significant factors that impact on health which can be broadly described as disease resistance (Figure 1). A mature gut flora competitively excludes gastro-intestinal pathogens (Abrams and Bishop, 1966; Nurmi and Rantala, 1973) the mechanisms of which are a vast field of study in themselves. Then there is the immune stimulation that a normal flora provides that generates protective innate and responsive immunity systems.

Animal nutrition has largely focused upon dietary impacts on productivity using gross measures such as feed conversion rate and meat to carcass ratio to assess the efficacy of diet formulations. This is clearly a complex art ensuring the correct

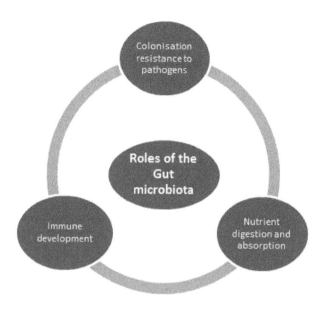

Figure 1. Simplified overview of the roles of the gut microbiota (drawn by Joy Leng)

energy balance, available protein and lipid, mineral content and so forth for each stage of the life cycle and desired outcome. The role of the gut microbiota has crucial influences on feed conversion and growth rates and yet our understanding of the gut microbiota is relatively limited. Also, the impact of the diet and the gut microbiota together on the physiological and metabolic impacts on the host is even less well understood. In addition, there has been a move to reduce prophylactic use of antibiotics in animal feed which, through implementation of EU directives for example, has been associated with a notable rise in endemic disease that impacts negatively on productivity. Finding alternative controls by dietary intervention is a high priority with consideration being given to probiotics, prebiotics, synbiotics and natural products such as plant derived oils. This chapter cannot cover all of these diverse aspects in depth, but will aim to focus upon the broader concepts of recent developments in the interrogation of the gut microbiota and host metabolome with particular reference to controlling gastro-intestinal disease.

The 'normal' gut microbiota

Jakobsson *et al.* (2015) showed that two C57BL/6 mice colonies maintained in near identical but separate conditions with identical diet and growth performance developed distinct gut microbiota and associated mucus thickness. An intriguing question from this study is how do different gut microbiotas develop despite the near identical nature of diet and environment? Studies of chickens have confirmed independently that chickens in the same flock with near identical diet and husbandry regimes show quite dramatic differences in gut microbiota (Sargeant *et al.*, 2014). However, one trend shown is an age effect with differing trajectories of microbiota development over time which is also noted in wild birds (Van Dongen *et al.*, 2013). Modern broilers have been shown to have a significantly higher amount of ileal lactobacilli and streptococcus than red jungle fowl when fed the same palm kernel meal based diet (Zulkifli *et al.*, 2009). However the high feed intake seen with domestication could account for this, such as has been seen when conventional broiler breeds have been compared to organic breeds (Bjerrum *et al.*, 2006). One question that arises is how different are the diets and microbiota of wild progenitor species compared with intensively reared and genetically bred modern production animals? A study comparing two modern breeds with a 1957 genetic line (Athens Canadian Random Bred) illustrated that the two modern breeds had communities that clustered together away from that seen in the 1957 line (Lumpkins *et al.*, 2010). The performance of the 1957 line was much poorer than the two modern breeds, potentially due to shorter villus height reducing absorptive capacity. When microbiota analyses were performed the two modern breeds were seen to have more Clostridia and less lactobacilli species than the 1957 line, which could have been associated with the improved performance. Wild birds are dependent on what is available during which seasons and the digestive tract of the birds shows adaptation to this (Lewin, 1963; Pulliainen and Tunkkari, 1983). A study investigating the difference between gut communities of wild and captive Western Capercaillie (Tetrao urogallus) illustrated that there were significant changes in community profiles during different seasons for the wild birds (Wienemann *et al.*, 2011). There was also a striking difference between the communities of wild and captive birds, with wild birds containing large numbers of Clostridiales, Actinobacteria and Bacteroidetes which were reduced or missing in the captive birds which, however, carried large numbers of sequences related to Anaerobiospirillium present. These differences could be related to the poorer caecal fermentation seen in captive birds (Wienemann *et al.*, 2011). With the caveat that there is variation among animals on the same apparent diet and husbandry regimes the interesting study by Wei *et al.* (2013) established what the consensus 'healthy' gut microbiota of chickens and turkeys is. They undertook a reductionist metadata analysis of available taxonomic studies of the gut microbiota generated by next generation sequencing approaches, the technicalities of which will be outlined later in this chapter, to identify core bacteria. This study identified 915 operational taxonomic units (OTUs), which for our purpose are species equivalents, in chickens and 464 OTUs turkeys. Firmicutes, Bacteroidetes, and Proteobacteria accounted for >90% of phyla and the predominant genera found in both chickens and turkeys were Clostridium, Ruminococcus, Lactobacillus, and Bacteroides. Table 1 gives a listing and identification of bacterial species in the chicken caecum from a recent study by Dragana *et al.* (2015) which correlate with Wei's metadata analysis. It is interesting to note that in the Dragana study faeces were collected also and analysed. Not unsurprisingly strict anaerobes declined in number whereas facultative anaerobes increased proportionately indicating faeces are not an ideal measure of the in vivo gut microbiota.

Similar studies have been undertaken in the pig to establish the 'healthy' gut microbiome. The early results of Leser *et al.* (2002), which have stood the test of time

Table 1. The 20 most abundant OTUs in chicken caecum

Closest culturable isolate	% in caecum	% in faeces
Bacteroides fragilis	14.1	1.2
Lactobacillus crispatus	11.3	15.4
Lactobacillus johnsonii	9.6	12.2
Lactobacillus salivarius	5.4	12.7
Lactobacillus reuteri	4.3	5.6
Acholeplasma palmae	3.9	0.5
Lactobacillus helveticus	3.5	8.6
Butyricicoccus pullicaecorum	3.4	0.2
Faecalibacterium prausnitzii	2.3	0.3
Lactobacillus vaginalis	1.3	0.8
Lactobacillus helveticus	1.2	2.7
Pontibacillus litoralis	0.9	0.2
Exiguobacterium acetylicum	0.9	0.1
Ruminococcus albus	0.9	0.1
Ruminococcus albus	0.8	0.1
Parabacteroides distasonis	0.8	0.0
Ruminococcus flavefaciens	0.8	0.1
Clostridium cellobioparum	0.7	0.1
Clostridium termitidis	0.7	0.1
Clostridium symbiosum	0.7	0.1

From Dragana *et al.* (2015). Sequences of the V4 region of the 16s rRNA gene were compared with those of known species on the metadata base and those sequencing 97% or greater similarity were named as the nearest culturable species even with improving technologies (Kim and Isaacson, 2015), demonstrated that 81% of the bacterial population belonged to the phyla Firmicutes and Bacteroidetes, with Prevotella and Bacteroides comprising 11.2% of genera. A recent study by Pajarillo *et al.* (2015) has added depth to our understanding of the dynamics of the gut microbiota related to genotype and mixing of animals. In a longitudinal study they showed differences between the gut microbiota of Duroc, Landrace and Yorkshire pure-bred lines. In addition they showed age related changes with an increasing proportion of the phylum Firmicutes correlating with decreasing the phylum Bacteroidetes over time, regardless of the purebred group. Furthermore, mixing of animals led to reduced diversity and greater similarity between the gut microbiota within and between pure-breeds. Yang *et al.* (2014) undertook a comparative cross-sectional study of the pig gut microbiota of Lantang, Bama, Erhualian, Meishan, Xiaomeishan, Duroc, Landrace, and Yorkshire sows and drew similar conclusions to Pajarillo *et al.* (2015) regarding the profile of the gut microbiota being influenced by breed. However, they also suggested that certain microbiota were positively correlated with lean animals (European) compared to obese types (Chinese).

Animals tend to have a finite productive cycle and the impact of age on the gut microbiota is as yet less well understood compared to that in humans (Zapata and Quigliarello, 2015; Lynch *et al.*, 2015). Our studies have shown a dramatic decline in diversity of the gut microbiota in spent layers compared with earlier stages in life (unpublished). Isaacson and Kim (2012, 2015) and Zhao *et al.* (2015) have shown the majority (>90%) of bacteria in the pig intestinal microbiome are from two Phyla: Firmicutes and Bacteroidetes, although there are subtle differences between breeds (Pajarillo *et al.*, 2014). Kim *et al.* (2015) confirmed observations regarding shifts in the pig microbiota with age and also with weight gain associated with a decrease in Bacteroidetes. However, they also found an increasing number of unclassifiable bacterial types emerging: these clearly need investigation. Using a non-NGS approach, Federici *et al.* (2015) showed part of the age process was an exchange of Methanobrevibacter smithii in early life with M. boviskoreani in later life: an interesting and presumed iso-functional shift however we are as yet unclear why this change occurs.

Early life events are crucial in development, and acquisition of the gut microbiota is of paramount importance. Mach *et al.* (2015) using NGS approaches showed, as previously demonstrated, Bacteroidetes and Firmicutes were the predominant phyla present at days 14, 36, 48, 60 and 70 after birth. Bacteroides, Oscillibacter, Escherichia/Shigella, Lactobacillus and unclassified Ruminococcaceae genera were prevalent in suckling piglets whereas Acetivibrio, Dialister, Oribacterium, Succinivibrio and Prevotella genera increased after weaning. Lactobacillus fermentum might be vertically transferred via breast milk or faeces. Significantly, although a single study group, the microbiota differentiated into two groups of lower and higher performing animals, the latter was positively correlated with increased abundance of Prevotella and with luminal secretory IgA concentrations and body weight. Conversely Scokker *et al.* (2015) demonstrated reduced diversity and altered profiles of the gut microbiota induced by early life antibiotic use and also stress induced by handling. Here are clues at the gut microbiota level as to how we can intervene to improve performance. As an example of one dietary intervention, Umu *et al.* (2015), knowing fibre properties such as solubility, fermentability, viscosity, and gel-forming ability varied between types, investigated the impact of resistant starch on microbiota of pigs. The relative abundance of Lachnospiraceae- and Ruminococcus-affiliated phylotypes increased with increasing resistant starch but the key metabolic pathways for starch degradation and other plant polysaccharides were unaffected, suggesting some genetic and metabolic redundancy.

What we can conclude is that there is no single 'normal' or 'healthy' gut microbiota as this is influenced by many factors including genotype, age, diet, season and husbandry practice indicating the gut microbiota is dynamic and responds to environmental influence. Most significantly however, is the fact that the gut microbiota is essential to maintain bodily functions and therefore has profound impacts on productivity and health and welfare of animals. However, from a nutritional point of view, the aim should be to produce diets that maintain the optimum gut microbiota. The challenge for the gut microbiologist is defining what that is in its many diverse forms and how it is best maintained!

Population analysis by Next Generation Sequencing

This chapter has presented the reader with a large number of named phyla, genera and even some species of bacteria. However, the taxonomy of the gut microbiota is a massive topic in its own right and cannot be dealt with here other than the briefest introduction to the main groupings cited thus far. The phylum Firmicutes comprise about 70% of the gut population in most animals and these comprise Gram +ve rod shaped bacteria that possess a low Guanosine and Cytosine content in their DNA (GC ratio) and include the spore forming genera of Bacilli and Clostridia. The next most abundant group of the gut population is the phylum Bacteroidetes that comprise about 12% in most animals. These are Gram –ve, anaerobic, rod shaped bacteria and include the genera Bacteroides, Flavobacteria, Flexibacteria, Rhodothermus, Sphingobacteria some of which are pathogenic such as Bacteroides fragilis. The phylum Proteobacteria comprising 10% of the gut microbiota is probably the best recognised of the gut associated bacteria being Gram –ve bacteria with a mid GC ratio harbouring many well characterised genera as Escherichia, Salmonella, Vibrio, Helicobacter amongst many others: many are pathogenic too. Until recently, analysis of these organisms was by culture and biochemical typing but so far only a minority of these organisms have been grown independently in the laboratory: we know little about the majority of bacteria that inhabit the guts of animals including ourselves. That said, recent advances in molecular technology allows us to sequence every single organism in the gut microbiota, true metagenome studies, or analyse the population by sequencing a single common gene found in all bacteria, true population profiling. Here we will give a brief overview of the principles of current genetic methodologies of next generation sequencing (NGS).

Microbial community profiling using Next Generation Sequencing approaches

Profiling microbial communities makes use of 'massively parallel' DNA sequencing. In short, to profile a community a target gene common to all members of the community is amplified by polymerase chain reaction and each amplicon or a large representation of the amplicon is sequenced individually. The most commonly used target is the gene encoding the 16S ribosomal ribonucleic acid (rRNA) gene: an rRNA species that is found in every bacterium that fulfils the role of being a scaffold for the ribosome, essential for protein synthesis. Other target genes can be used such as the genes encoding the gyrases, enzymes that are essential for DNA replication. Key to the target gene selection is that these have regions of high homology as well as regions of dissimilarity that reflect their evolutionary history. The regions of homology reflect functionality which in the case of the 16S rRNA gene is RNA-RNA folding and RNA-protein binding and these tend to be relatively invariant between bacterial species as they have to fulfil their scaffold function. PCR can be designed with primers that anneal with these 'conserved' regions of homology of the encoding gene to ensure effective PCR amplification; the usefulness of the sequences comes in the ability to align sequences and compare the 'variable' regions. The differences in these variable regions aid recognition of different bacterial phyla, potentially genera and sometimes, although rarely, species. The 16S rRNA gene is 1,500 base pairs long and contains nine hypervariable regions (v1-9), which are the targets for bacterial community sequencing (Figure 2).

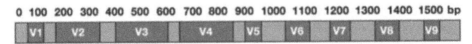

Figure 2. 16S rRNA gene linear structure. Acknowledge Joy Leng for preparation of diagram

The technology of sequencing is moving apace and this is not the place to describe each system (Roche 454, MiSeq Illumina, IonTorrent and many others) in detail but rather focus on the principles of the process and data handling. Fortunately the alphabet of the genetic sequence makes use of only four nucleotides (A, T, G, C) and the DNA double helix is made of two antiparallel strands held together by H-bonds between the nucleotides with A opposite T and G opposite C. With the MiSeq Illumina system as one exemplar, PCR amplicons are melted to give single stranded DNA which are diluted into flow cells to give just one strand per cell and then anchored by annealing to a short single stranded target oligonucleotide: this recognises either a tag on the primer or the primer itself. Reverse complementary strands are generated by DNA polymerase and the original strand is washed away. Complementary fluorescently labelled nucleotides are then added to the anchored parallel strands. Each type of nucleotide base has a different fluorescent terminator dye and these are imaged and cleaved when the nucleotide is added (Figure 3). All four types of terminator bound nucleotides are present during this processing, which allows for natural competition and reducing bias. This occurs simultaneously to millions of DNA strands in different cells allowing generation of a large number of sequencing reads.

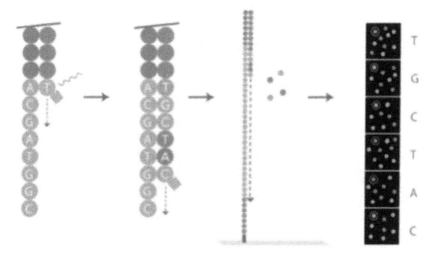

Figure 3. Schematic showing sequencing by synthesis, part of Illumina sequencing technology (modified from http://www.dkfz.de). Acknowledge Joy Leng for preparation of diagram.

The technology is impressive delivering potentially millions of sequence reads across a defined short region of the target. The next step is to compare each read and a commonly used programme is QIIME (Quantitative insights into microbial ecology), an open-source bioinformatics pipeline that is ideal for processing and analysing large quantities of raw sequencing data. Again, here is not the place to go into fine detail but to give a simplified overview. The object of the processing (bioinformatics) is to ensure you are reading the same sequence from the same target source, filtering out poor quality sequence and then aligning the sequences with target genes already sequenced and available on databases. The key output by these complex statistical comparisons is to give a sequence a value of similarity with a known sequence which defines closeness to a specific OTU. This is gross over-simplification but the output can be as simple as a table of each sequence with a score of similarity to a defined OTU: the discriminatory power can be adjusted by setting comparison to 95-99% similarity for example: the higher the similarity the greater the accuracy of OTU assignment. Having achieved this, it is possible to see the data represented in a number of ways such as 'alpha rarefaction' that describes the bacterial diversity within the bacterial community of one sample whereas 'beta rarefaction' describes the difference in bacterial diversity between samples and this can be readily visualised as a principal coordinates (PCoA) plot. Also the data can be presented as a 'Taxomomic Summary' that gives the percentage of total reads that have been assigned to any bacterial phylum, order or class. Thereafter there are many visual means of displaying the information and one example is given in Figure 4.

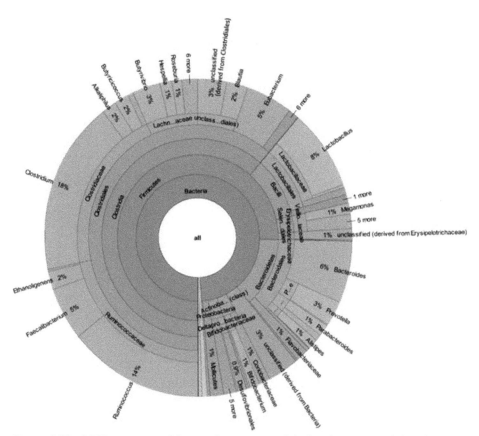

Figure 4. The OTU assignment of the caecal gut content of chicken from Wei *et al.* (2013).

This approach allows exploration of community dynamics, diversity indices and sequence information and can be considered as metataxonomics, or population profiling. Metagenomics on the other hand is the study of all the genomes within an environmental sample by using genetic and bioinformatics technologies. Most commonly it is used to describe the gene content of all bacteria within a niche, whether this be in soil or the gut of a mammal.

So what can we conclude from this quantum technological leap? Certainly we now have powerful interrogative tools to define populations by longitudinal and cross-sectional studies in any animal species. We can also define the entire gene set, the metagenome, of the gut microbiota and the relative abundance of genes governing particular metabolic competences: although the vast majority of genes have yet to be defined in real terms and most will have a role inferred from gene similarities with genes of known function from well-defined species. However, using these tools we can assess population shifts and by assaying messenger RNA (mRNA) in transcription studies we can further define which genes are expressed in response to the myriad of variables we have already discussed. From the perspective of the animal nutritionist, there seem to be two keys aims, one is to maintain if not improve the gut microbiota to achieve best health status and growth and, the other is to rebalance the gut microbiota after perturbations that may be caused many factors including disease, stresses, treatment with antibiotics, and diet. The next section focuses upon control of disease.

Resistance to infection and manipulating the gut microbiota to enhance resistance

There are many pathogens causing gastrointestinal illnesses and most are risks at certain stages in the development of the animal, with infections common at times of stress and change notably at parturition and hatching, at post-weaning and at maturation associated with hormonal changes especially for poultry coming into lay. The list of pathogens is far too long to discuss here but Salmonella enterica subsp., Escherichia coli, Campylobacter spp, Brachyspira spp and Clostridium perfringens are relevant bacterial exemplars. Many are pathogenic in animals and several are zoonotic passing down the food chain to infect man also. Each causes disease in broadly the same way after ingestion, colonisation of the GI tract, disturbance of the epithelium often by secretion of toxins or other biological effect, and induction of diarrhoea due to energy and salt imbalances induced by cellular disturbances. Some pathogens are highly invasive and may have a systemic phase causing fever such as several serotypes of Salmonella.

Abrams and Bishop (1966) described the effect of the normal microbial flora on resistance of the small intestine to infection although it was the paper of Nurmi and Rantala (1973) that described protection from Salmonella infection in newly hatched chicks pre-dosed with faeces from healthy mature adult chickens that formalised the phenomenon of competitive exclusion. Returning to the studies of Jakobsson *et al.* (2015), they showed that two C57BL/6 mice colonies developed distinct gut microbiota that correlated with mucus thickness and disease resistance. One, harbouring increased numbers of Erysipelotrichi, produced thick mucus that was impenetrable to pathogenic bacteria. The other, harbouring increased numbers of Proteobacteria and TM7 bacteria, produced thin mucus that was penetrable to pathogenic bacteria. Other than the mucins, another natural barrier to infection is production of antibodies by the gut-associated lymphoid tissues (GALT) which again the normal gut microbiota influences and can be enhanced by addition of probiotics in the diet. A current definition of probiotics is "live micro-organisms which, when administered in adequate amounts, confer a health benefit on the host" (WHO, 2001). These bacteria are non-pathogenic and non-toxigenic, can withstand storage, can survive the conditions in the small bowel and stomach and readily colonise the lower gut. Haghighi *et al.* (2006) demonstrated enhanced immune responses when chicks were dosed from one day of age with a range of probiotics that gave rise to intestinal antibodies reactive with a number of bacterial toxins. Probiotics may also induce innate immunity, bind pathogens or interfere with their metabolism by acid production and/or toxin secretion. For example, adherence of Lactobacillus acidophilus and a few Bifidobacteria to large bowel cells prevents binding of and colonisation by pathogens such as enterotoxigenic and enteropathogenic Escherichia coli (Macfarlane, 1999). A detailed review of probiotics for use in animals was undertaken by Collins *et al.* (2009). However a more recent meta-analysis of probiotics used for the specific control of Salmonella species in chickens was undertaken by Kerr *et al.* (2013). Although there are many exemplars of success, Kerr *et al.* (2003) concluded, "Out of the various interventions to reduce Salmonella colonization in broilers on-farm, CE was the most studied; its inability to be licenced in certain countries and proof of consistent efficacy remains a barrier." One of the biggest knowledge gaps relates to the impact of probiotics on the entire gut microbiome and the exact mechanism of pathogen reduction in vivo: inferring acid sensitivity of pathogens exposed to probiotic supernatants, although used as a selection criterion for development of probiotics, is trivial and naïve.

Antibiotics are chemical substances that control bacteria either by killing them (bactericidal) or blocking function (bacteristatic). A problem with the use of antibiotics is that over time bacteria develop resistance against them and moreover, using antibiotics can kill both harmful and beneficial bacteria thereby causing depletion of the normal gut microbiota and sometimes antibiotic induced diarrhoea [AID]. Kim *et al.* (2012) demonstrated dramatic microbiota shifts and reduced diversity by tylosin when administered in feed to pigs. The paper of Cox *et al.* (2014) highlights the impact of chemotherapy in disrupting the intestinal microbiota that should be a stable complex community required to fulfil its role in animal production. They showed that low dose penicillin induced not only changes in the microbiota, but also significant metabolic changes which changed the phenotype of the host animal: this will be examined in detail later. Here is a very significant issue for animal nutritionists and veterinarians. In the EU, the year 2006 saw the implementation of directives banning the use of in-fed antibiotics for prophylaxis. Growth advantage by antibiotic supplementation is well recognised, but the aim of the ban was to reduce emergence of resistant bacteria of human health significance. This is laudable but the consequences for the health and productivity of animals with the re-emergence of endemic diseases has resulted in continued use of antibiotics chemotherapeutically. So there has been a major research effort to find alternatives that suppress disease caused by the common endemic production diseases. To give an early example of alternatives to antibiotics, Shim *et al.* (2005) investigated replacement of antibiotics in feed with probiotics, prebiotics and mixture of the two, synbiotics in piglets. In a more recent example, Cartman *et al.* (2008) developed B. subtilis spore probiotics that reduced C. perfringens colonisation in poultry. They showed that although aerobic, these probiotics germinate in the gut and it seems this process is associated with reducing C. perfringens numbers. Mappley *et al.* (2011, 2013) developed Lactobacillus reuteri and salivarius probiotics that suppressed Brachyspira pilosicoli colonisation in poultry, the cause of avian intestinal spirochaetosis, and seemed to contribute to improved overall health. Searle *et al.* (2009, 2010) investigated the potential of the prebiotic GOS in controlling Salmonella showing both physical protection from invasion by Salmonella and some immune stimulation by the long chain fraction of GOS. Here we should define prebiotics: Roberfroid, (2000) defined them as "indigestible fermented food substrates that selectively stimulate the growth, composition, and activity of microflora in gastrointestinal tract and thus improve hosts' health and well-being". There are many such compounds including Galacto-oligosaccharides (GOS), Fructo-oligosaccgarides (FOS), mannanoligosaccharides (MOS), Inulin and others. Shim *et al.* (2005) showed that these interventions increased the number of Bifidobacteria, reduced the number of Enterobacteriaceae, increased feed conversion, and enhanced the structural integrity of the gut as assessed by histological analysis of villus height and width. As some interventions enhance immune responsiveness, one possibility is enhancement of vaccine responses. A study by Lourenço *et al.* (2015) showed that supplementation of the chick diet with MOS increased CD3+, CD4+, CD8+, and goblet cell counts in the intestines of broilers vaccinated and challenged with Salmonella Enteritidis.

Vaccination is well established for the major economically important diseases in both chicks and pigs, but for many of the re-emerging endemic diseases the cost benefit of developing vaccines is questionable and alternatives are needed. Perhaps one exception worth considering is colibacillosis in poultry caused by avian pathogenic *E. coli* for which vaccine intervention has been developed (La Ragione *et al.*, 2013) and deployed commercially with success. There are many novel approaches to vaccination that over time are likely to be deployed, with the move toward single shot multivalent vaccines being the 'holy grail'. However, we come back to the cost benefit for such developments to become realisable.

Other than pro- and prebiotics, plant extracts could present an alternative solution to replace conventional chemical antimicrobials in treating intestinal diseases (Soković et al., 2010). Ancient civilizations used plant extracts for medicinal purposes and for food preservation (Al-Turki, 2007). Evidence suggests that Neanderthals used plants such as hollyhock around 60,000 years ago in what is now Iraq and these plants are still being used in ethno-medicine to this day (Cowan, 1999). Ancient Egyptians used willow bark to reduce the symptoms of headaches and fever and centuries later, scientists found that the bark contained salicylic acid which is now widely used in aspirin (Thomson, 1978; Stockwell, 1988). Plants have an extensive range of secondary metabolites, "substances produced by an organism that are not part of its normal growth" that have many useful properties including being antiseptic, anti-inflammatory and antimicrobial (Martin and Ernst, 2003; Lixandru et al., 2010; Mazid et al., 2011). The range of plant secondary metabolites and some of their properties are shown in table 2. Evidence for the antimicrobial effects of plants is well established and there is a vast literature. By way of example, Tayel and El-Tras (2009) used twenty five herbs and spices (including basil, lemongrass, clove, and cinnamon) against seven bacterial strains. These all demonstrated significant antimicrobial activities against most of the strains which are responsible for food poisoning. Although there are a plethora of *in vitro* tests of this type the question for the nutritionist is their use in vivo and for what desired outcome: here are a few selected examples of in vivo efficacy of phytochemicals. Phenols and phenolic acids are phytochemicals consisting of one phenolic ring (Mandal *et al.*, 2010), commonly found in fruits and vegetables (Vinson *et al.*, 2001). Eugenol, Cinnamic acid and Caffeic acid have wide antimicrobial effects and are found in clove, tarragon and thyme that can be added to feed. However, the flavonoids are considered in human health as 'wonder drugs' and foods containing them as 'super foods'. The review by Middleton *et al.* (2000) covers these in depth especially *in vitro* cell studies indicating roles in combating inflammation, heart disease and cancer in humans. In chickens these compounds have been shown to improve meat quality, the electrophysiology of the gut barrier and to enhance immune responses (Awad *et al.*, 2011; Kamboh and Zhu, 2013a,b; Hager-Theodorides *et al.*, 2014). Saponins are similarly considered one of the most important classes of natural plant products consisting of a steroid aglycone with one or more sugar units attached at different positions (Osbourn *et al.*, 2011). The two classes of steroidal saponins, spirostanol and furostanol saponins, have anticancer properties exerting a broad range of pharmacological activities such as expectorant, anti-inflammatory, vaso-protective, antifungal and anti-parasitic effects. Terpinols are the scent of plants (essential oil) and consequently are used for their aroma. They have a chemical structure of (C10H16)n and arise as diterpenes (C20), triterpenes (C30) and tetraterpenes (C40) (Gershenzon and Dudareva, 2007). These essential oils from eucalyptus and peppermint have been demonstrated to control the most prevalent Eimeria spp. involved in coccidiosis of broiler chicken, improving production, alleviating lesions and reducing intestinal oocyst counts (Barbour *et al.*, 2015). However, there is an established literature describing the negative impacts of these compounds when fed to chickens giving rise to poor growth and reduced egg weight (Griminger and Fisher, 1958; Heywang *et al.*, 1959). Adverse effects have been observed also with other plant derived products such as condensed tannins that can bind to the cell walls of ruminal bacteria, stopping their growth and reducing their protease activity (Hagerman *et al.*, 1997).

Table 2. Plant derived antimicrobials and health related phytochemicals. Adapted from (Cowan, 1999)

Class	Subclass	Mechanism
Phenolics	• Simple phenols • Phenolic acids • Quinines	• Substrate deprivation • Bind to adhesins • Complex with cell wall • Inactive enzymes • Membrane disruption
	• Flavonoids • Flavanones	• Bind to adhesins • Complex with cell wall • Inactive enzymes
	• Tannins	• Bind to proteins • Bind to adhesins • Enzyme inhibition • Substrate deprivation
Terpenoids		• Membrane disruption
Alkaloids		• Intercalate into cell wall and/ or DNA
Saponins		• Anticancer/ inhibiting the tumour

There is an extensive literature on the many classes of phytochemical for use in human and animal health. Unlike human studies, there is still an overriding empirical approach to the use and application of potentially beneficial plant derived products in animal production. There are still few studies that take an holistic or system biology approach to unravelling the complexity of action of these potentially highly valuable products. Crucial to their selection, development and deployment is pragmatic science that describes their impact on the gut microbiota and the host metabolome.

Recent studies using animal models to understand the human condition

Novel insights are being gained by the use of animal models to study various human conditions such as obesity, diabetes, blood pressure, neurology, Crohn's, IBS and here just a few are highlighted as exemplars because such approaches are likely to yield value for the animal nutritionist. Slezak *et al.* (2014) demonstrated that gut length was influenced by the genetics of the mouse but heavily influenced by the gut mocrobiota. Specifically, gnotobiotic mice fed a limited human gut microbiota (SIHUMI) had small intestines that were significantly shorter by between 9 and 16% depending on mouse genotype than those of the gnotobiotic controls. These authors went on to examine the association of gut length with microbial production of polyamines and short-chain fatty acids that are important intestinal growth factors: putrescine, spermine, spermidine, N-acetylspermine, acetate, propionate, and butyrate concentrations were much higher in SIHUMI mice. Whether these contributed to the gut length is however under debate. Turnbaugh *et al.* (2006) and Murphy *et al.* (2010) demonstrated obesity is associated with changes in the relative abundance of the two dominant bacterial divisions, the Bacteroidetes and the Firmicutes, in humans and in mice instilled with the microbiota from lean and obese human donors. Biochemical analyses suggested that obese microbiomes harvested energy from the diet considerably more efficiently from lean microbiomes and that this phenotype can be transferred readily to germ-free mice generating increased total body fat in those mice. Similar bacterial shifts were observed by Larsen *et al.* (2010) who demonstrated reduced Firmicutes and Clostridia and altered ratios of Bacteroidetes to Firmicutes in diabetic humans with changes correlating to blood glucose levels. Significantly, Cani *et al.* (2009) showed mice on high fat diets generating 'obese' and 'diabetic' human gut microbiota can reverse these metabolic impacts by increasing the numbers of Bifidobacteria simply through addition of prebiotics to their diet. Recent studies using pigs, cloned to reduce genetic variability, also showed the same microbiota changes and weight gain as for mice and humans on lean and obese diets (Pedersen *et al.*, 2013). Using the mouse model Joyce *et al.* (2014) investigated the role of the microbiota on host energy metabolism and adiposity by gene regulation studies focussing on expression of key microbial genes in bile salt metabolism. They demonstrated that high-level expression of bacterial bile salt hydrolase (BSH) in conventionally reared mice induced significant reduction in host weight gain, plasma cholesterol, and liver triglycerides, demonstrating the overall impact of elevated BSH activity on host physiology. There is good experimental evidence from several animal studies showing that changes in dietary iron availability alter the gut microbiota community structure. Werner *et al.* (2011) demonstrated in a rodent model of Crohn's ileitis that removal of ferrous sulphate altered the gut microbiota and reduced ileitis. Pereira *et al.* (2015) demonstrated in a rodent model reduced iron severely depleted the diversity of the microbiota that could be partially reversed by addition of nano-particulate iron. McVey-Neufeld *et al.* (2013) compared neuronal functioning of the myenteric plexus in gnotobiotic and conventional mice and showed that commensal intestinal microbiota are necessary for normal excitability of gut sensory neurons thus providing a potential mechanism for the transfer of information between the microbiota and nervous system. What these diverse exemplar studies show is the importance of the gut microbiota in normal functioning of its host and that diet can alter the microbiota both negatively, high fat diet for example, or recovery to normality, prebiotic application for example.

Production impacts of probiotics, prebiotics and phytochemical in animals

There is a desire to combine outcomes of intervention, such as improve a specific nutritional characteristic as well as contribute to weight gain and pathogen suppression. For example, Tako *et al.* (2014) aimed to assess the effect of prebiotics from wheat on Fe bioavailability in vivo in broiler chickens. Although a little ambiguous, the treatment induced higher numbers of Bifidobacteria and Lactobacillus species although Fe availability was not enhanced. Also it is well known that other probiotics have productivity advantages such as Lactobacillus agilis JCM 1048 and L. salivarius subsp. salicinius JCM 1230 described by Thi *et al.* (2003) who showed that dosing chicks with these strains not only resulted in significant weight gains compared to untreated controls but was associated also with increased prevalence of other Lactobacillus species with concomitant reduction in Enterobacteriaceae. However, the response of chicks to probiotic interventions is variable. Gérard *et al.* (2008) showed dosing with Lactobacillus species reduced C. perfringens but showed no impact on either other Lactic Acid Bacteria (LAB) or Enterobacteriaceae.

There are a plethora of differing outcomes from chicks dosed with probiotics and many early studies made use of in situ hybridisation and temporal temperature gradient gel electrophoresis techniques to assess population shifts. These are not as detailed as population analyses by 16S rRNA gene analysis and there is a clear need to use next generation sequencing methods to increase our understanding. Also, many probiotics have positive metabolic impacts on the host and Table 3 shows a list of a number commercially available probiotics and the animal sector and claims for use.

Apart from replacement of antibiotics, the use of various probiotics has been investigated for induction of specific properties. However, caution in selection must be shown. For example Bjerg *et al.* (2014) demonstrated by feeding trials and infused gut experiments that Lactobacillus paracasei subsp paracasei L. casei W8 suppressed energy uptake through lower food intake significantly and although the

Table 3. Some commercially available probiotics and the health benefits indicated. From Collins et al. (2009)

Product name	Probiotic organism	Culture collection	Target organism
Adjulact 2000 ®	*Streptococcus infantarius* *Lactobacillus plantarum*	CNCM I-841 CNCM I-840	Calves
Bactocell ®	*Pediococcus acidilactici*	CNCM MA 18/5	Broilers
Biacton ®	*Lactobacillus farciminis*	CNCM MA 67/4	Piglets
Bioplus 2B ®	*Bacillus licheniformis* *Bacillus subtilis*	DSM 5749 DSM 5750	Piglets / pigs for fattening Broilers, calves and piglets / pigs for fattening
Biosprint ®	*Saccharomyces cerevisiae*	BCCM / MUCL 39885	Beef cattle and piglets / pigs for fattening
Bonvital ®	*Enterococcus faecium* *Lactobacillus rhamnosus*	DSM 7134 DSM 7133	Calves and pigs for fattening
Biosaf SC 47 ®	*Saccharomyces cerevisiae*	NCYC Sc 47	Beef / dairy cattle and piglets / pigs
Cylactin LBC ®	*Enterococcus faecium*	NCIMB 10415	Broilers and calves and piglets / pigs for fattening
Fecinor plus ®	*Enterococcus faecium*	CECT 4515	Calves / beef cattle and piglets / pigs for fattening
Gardion ®	*Lactobacillus casei* *Enterococcus faecium*	NCIMB 30096 NCIMB 30098	Calves
Kluyten ®	*Kluyveromyces Marxiamus*	MUCL 39434	Dairy cattle
Lactiferm ®	*Enterococcus faecium*	NCIMB 11181	Calves and piglets
L.acidophilus D2/CSL ®	*Lactobacillus acidophilus*	CECT 4529	Broilers / laying hens
Levucell SB20 ®	*Saccharomyces cerevisiae*	CNCM I-1079	Piglets / pigs
Levucell SC20 ®	*Saccharomyces cerevisiae*	CNCM I-1077	Beef / dairy cattle
Microferm ®	*Enterococcus faecium*	DSM 5464	Broilers, calves and piglets
Mirimil-Biomin ®	*Enterococcus faecium*	DSM 3520	Calves
Oralin	*Enterococcus faecium*	NCIMB 10415	Broilers, calves and pigs for fattening
Primver Pro ®	*Enterococcus mundtii*	CNCM MA 27/4	Lambs
Probios PDFM Granular ®	*Enterococcus faecium* *Enterococcus faecium*	DSM 4788 DSM 4789	Broilers
Yea-Sacc ®	*Saccharomyces cerevisiae*	CBS 493 94	Calves / beef / dairy cattle

mechanism for this is not fully elucidated they did show alteration of expression of the glucagon encoding gene (GCG) in the probiotic fed group. The article by Missoten *et al.* (2015) brings together the evidence for use of fermented feeds having dramatic benefits on all ages of pig production cycle. Fermentation leads to acidification that kills pathogens and increases the number of beneficial Lactic Acid Bacteria and Bifidobacteria. Although the evidence presented is good there is still a dearth of gut microbiota population analysis associated with such studies and even fewer regarding the metabolic changes and impact on the host metabolome.

Measuring the metabolic impact in the gut and the host

It is well known that pro- and prebiotics are beneficial to the host but there has been a realisation that our understanding of the underlying mechanisms is limited. Recent reviews (Park *et al.*, 2013; Pan and Yu, 2014), as does this essay, identify the need to apply the latest systems biology approaches to define not only shifts in the gut population and its gene content and expression but also utilise various tools such as ultra-high pressure liquid chromatography-mass spectroscopy profiling and nuclear magnetic resonance technologies to define the metabolic implications of these shifts. Here, we will discuss briefly one tool for analysing the metabolic impact of the microbiota on the luminal content of the gut and the metabolites that enter the host blood that circulates to the liver to become deposited in tissues, namely nuclear magnetic resonance (NMR), true metabonomics. As commented by Vogt *et al.* (2015) there is a two-way chemical dialogue between the host and its gut microbiota largely through primary and secondary metabolites that create a specific gut environment that is of mutual benefit to both. However, many pathogens have subverted these chemical signals so that several of these metabolites including short-chain fatty acids, succinate, mucin O-glycans and secondary bile acids have become signals that affect the growth and virulence of pathogens. In short, it is essential to understand fully the benefit and potential dis-benefits of any nutritional intervention!

Nuclear magnetic resonance (NMR) spectroscopy

NMR spectroscopy is used to profile hundreds of small metabolites within a biofluid or tissue sample by using an electromagnetic field. Atoms such as 1H and 13C with differing numbers of protons and electrons possess an overall spin state which generates a small electrical current. A nucleus possessing spin can have two orientations: one with higher and one with lower energy. Spin comes in multiples of ½ and can be positive (higher energy) or negative (lower energy), for example a 1H nucleus can have two spin states; +½ or -½. In the absence of an external magnetic field these have equal energy, giving a net spin of 0 but application of an electromagnetic field separates these two energy levels. The number of nuclei in each spin state is determined by the Boltzman distribution which states there will always be an excess of nuclei in the lower energy state than the higher energy state.

Exciting nuclei with electromagnetic radiation shifts low energy nuclei into the higher energy level but when the applied electromagnetic radiation is removed (pulsed) the nuclei relax back to their original energy state and emit a small magnetic field. This feature is measured in the NMR spectrometer and determines the unique signal emitted by each nucleus as it relaxes back to equilibrium, the free induction decay (FID). This produces a spectrum containing individual peaks the position of which is dependent on the electrons surrounding the nucleus, and thereby can be used to identify metabolites within a sample. For all analysis samples must run with an internal standard, such as tetramethylsilane (TMS) or 3-trimethylsilyl-1-[2,2,3,3-2H4] propionate (TSP). NMR standards give a single strong 1H resonance as all of their nuclei have identical protons. Signal intensity is proportional to molar concentration of the molecule in the sample. Examples of hydrogens within compounds that produce different chemical shifts can be seen in Figure 5. It is possible to compare sample profiles to assess what metabolite changes have resulted from any applied change, such as a dietary intervention. This approach can be applied also to the luminal contents of the gut, the blood plasma, liver and muscle.

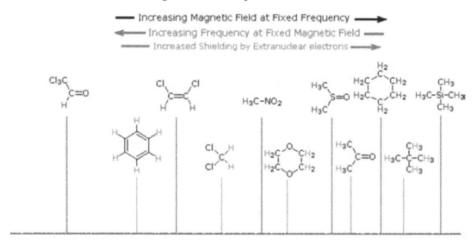

Figure 5. Resonance signals from different compounds, showing the chemical shift of protons in different environments. On the far right is tetramethylsilane (TMS), an NMR standard with a chemical shift of 0 (http://www2.chemistry.msu.edu).

Ji *et al.* (2012) used a metabonomic approach to investigate the basis resulting from genetic selection of chickens for the rapid accumulation of adipose tissue. They identified metabolic pathways associated with fat accretion indicating these could be targets for future genetic selection or management practices to control fat content. Stanley *et al.* (2013) indicated from their studies that broilers fed a wheat-soya diet had distinct gut microbiota associated with apparent metabolisable energy (AME: difference between energy consumed and energy excreted). They showed birds with higher numbers of bacteria able to break-down cellulose and resistant starch were more energy efficient whereas poor performers had many untypable phylotypes belonging to the Firmicutes: whether these would be useful for human weight control is worth investigating. Baéza *et al.* (2015) took these observations further using a metabolomics approach to attempt to identify plasma markers of AME determining betaine, glutamine, and histidine were the most discriminating metabolites between high and low AME groups. One study using a metabolomics approach clearly demonstrated the different metabolite profiles found in breast meat from chickens treated with amoxicillin compared with those without (Hermo *et al.*, 2014) reinforcing the rules on antibiotic withdrawal periods prior to slaughter. The authors indicated that antibiotic treatment has long lasting effects on meat quality and suggested that current withdrawal periods may be inadequate. For the pig, it is known that the ratio of fermentable carbohydrate (fCHO) and protein (fCP) influences the pig microbiota and Pieper *et al.* (2012) demonstrated an increased abundance of arachidonic acid metabolism derivatives in the luminal contents of the colon of pigs fed a high concentration of fCP irrespective of dietary fCHO. Straadt *et al.* (2014) used NMR to profile the meat of different cross breeds in an attempt to correlate the biochemical profile with flavour: alanine, carnosine, isoleucine, methionine, phenylalanine, valine, lactate, inosine monophosphate (IMP), inosine, glycerol and choline-containing compounds were found to be significantly affected by crossbreed.

And what of the future?

This chapter has given a variety of examples of simple dietary intervention all aimed at improvements in the production and health of animals. Technological advances now provide tools for deeper systems biological approaches not only to better understand the impact of these interventions but also to provide the pragmatic science to develop more informed approaches. We have seen that there is no one ideal gut microbiota, which provides added complexity especially as even in carefully management flocks and herds there is significant animal to animal variability relating to factors not yet defined. Is there a core gut bacterial population that can be detected and maintained? The evidence suggests there is much gene and metabolic redundancy in the gut microbiota so perhaps we should focus on gene pathways and metabolic outcomes rather than specific bacteria. We also have the added complication that the gut microbiota evolves with age and diet and is heavily influenced by the host genotype suggesting senescence that perhaps we should aim to reverse or that this is a natural progression that we should aim to manage over time. We have also seen some evidence relating to specific metabolic outcomes that are influenced by the gut microbiota which in terms of animal production relate directly to such measures as FCR and AME. However, we also need to focus on the products and the specific nutritional attributes these have for the final end user, which for the case of production animals is the human consumer. The potential exists to have designer products with added value nutritional benefits such as reduced cholesterol in red meats, omega-3 oil in non-fish products, and also products with specific organoleptic and satiety profiles. We should also be considering the input into animal feed. With increasing competition for nutrients between humans and animals, sustainability has become our watch word. Can we replace traditional feed components with novel ingredients that have beneficial impacts on animals and human health? Although this chapter has touched upon gut metagenomics and metabonomics as newer tools in unravelling these complexities, we must consider a true systems approach to take into account environmental and management factors as well as climate change.

References

Abrams, G.D. and Bishop, J.E. (1966). Effect of the normal microbial flora on the resistance of the small intestine to infection. *Journal of Bacteriology*, **92**, 1604-1608.

Al-Turki, A. (2007) Antibacterial effect of thyme, peppermint, sage, black pepper and garlic hydrosols against Bacillus subtilis and Salmonella enteritidis. *Journal of Food, Agriculture and Environment*, **5**, 92-94.

Awad, W.A., Ghareeb, K. and Bohm, J. (2011). Evaluation of the chicory inulin efficacy on ameliorating the intestinal morphology and modulating the intestinal electrophysiological properties in broiler chickens. *Journal of Animal Physiology and Animal Nutrition*, **95**, 65-72.

Baéza, E., Jégou, M., Gondret, F., Lalande-Martin, J., Tea, I., Le Bihan-Duval, E., Berri, C., Collin, A., Métayer-Coustard, S., Louveau, I., Lagarrigue, S. and Duclos, M.J. (2015). Pertinent plasma indicators of the ability of chickens to synthesize and store lipids. *Journal of Animal Science*, **93**, 107-116.

Barbour, E.K., Bragg, R.R., Karrouf, G., Iyer, A., Azhar, E., Harakeh, S. and Kumosani, T. (2015). Control of eight predominant Eimeria spp. involved in economic coccidiosis of broiler chicken by a chemically characterized essential oil. *Journal of Applied Microbiology*, **118**, 583-91.

Bjerg, A.T., Kristensen, M., Ritz, C., Holst, J.J., Rasmussen, C., Leser, T.D., Wellejus, A. and Astrup, A. (2014). Lactobacillus paracasei subsp paracasei L. casei W8 suppresses energy intake acutely. *Appetite*, **82**, 111-118.

Bjerrum, L., Enberg, R.M., Leser, T.D., Jensen, B.B., Finster, K. and Pedersen, K. (2006). Microbial community composition of the ileum and cecum of broiler chickens was revealed by molecular and culture-based techniques. *Poultry Science*, **85**, 1151-1164.

Cani, P.D., Possemiers, S., Van de Wiele, T., Guiot, Y., Everard, A., Rottier, O., Geurts, L., Naslain, D., Neyrinck, A., Lambert, D.M., Muccioli, G.C. and Delzenne, N.M. (2009). Changes in gut microbiota control inflammation in obese mice through a mechanism involving GLP-2-driven improvement of gut permeability. *Gut*, **58**, 1091-1103.

Cartman, S.T., La Ragione, R.M. and Woodward, M.J. (2008). Bacillus subtilis spores germinate in the chicken gastrointestinal tract. *Applied and Environmental Microbiology*, 74, 5254-5248.

Collins, J.W., La Ragione, R.M., Woodward, M.J. and Searle, L.E.J. (2009). Applications of Prebiotics and Probiotics in Livestock. In: *Prebiotics and Probiotics Science and Technology*. Eds Charalampopoulous and Rastall Springer New York ISBN 978-0-387-79057-2. pp 1123-1192.

Cowan, M. (1999) Plant products as antimicrobial agents. *Clinical Microbiology Reviews*, 12, 564-582.

Cox, L.M., Yamanishi, S., Sohn, J., Alekseyenko, A.V., Leung, J.M., Cho, I., Kim, S.G., Li, H., Gao, Z., Mahana, D., Zárate Rodriguez, J.G., Rogers, A.B., Robine, N., Loke, P. and Blaser, M.J. (2014) Altering the intestinal microbiota during a critical developmental window has lasting metabolic consequences. *Cell*, 158, 705-21.

Dragana, S., Geier, M.S., Chen, H., Hughes, R.J. and Moore R.J. (2015). Comparison of fecal and cecal microbiotas reveals qualitative similarities but quantitative differences. *BMC Microbiology*, doi:10.1186/s12866-015-0388-6.

Federici, S., Miragoli, F., Pisacane, V., Rebecchi, A., Morelli, L. and Callegari, M.L. (2015). Archael microbiota population in piglet feces shifts in response to weaning: *Methanobrevibacter smithii* is replaced with *Methanobrevibacter boviskoreani*. *FEMS Microbiology Letters*, 362, 678-684.

Gérard, P., Brézillon, C., Quéré, F., Salmon, A. and Rabot, S. (2008). Characterization of Cecal Microbiota and Response to an Orally Administered Lactobacillus Probiotic Strain in the Broiler Chicken. *Journal of Molecular Microbiology and Biotechnology*, 14, 115–122

Gershenzon, J. and Dudareva, N. (2007). The function of terpene natural products in the natural world. *Nature Chemical Biology*, 3, 408-14.

Gill, S.R., Pop, M., DeBoy, R.T., Eckburg, P.B., Turnbaugh, P.J., Samuel, S., Gordon, J.I., Relman, D.A., Fraser-Liggett, C.M. and Nelson, K.E. (2006). Metagenomic Analysis of the Human Distal Gut Microbiome. *Science*, 312, 1355-1359.

Hagerman, A., Zhao, Y. and Johnson, S. (1997). Antinutrients and Phytochemicals in Food. United States of America. *Journal of the American Chemical Society*, 662.

Hager-Theodorides, A.L., Goliomytis, M., Delis, S. and Deligeorgis, S. (2014). Effects of dietary supplementation with quercetin on broiler immunological characteristics. *Animal Feed Science and Technology*, 198, 224–230.

Haghighi, H.R., Gong, J., Gyles, C.L., Anthony Hayes, M., Zhou, H., Sanei, B., Chambers, J.R. and Sharif, S. (2006). Probiotics Stimulate Production of Natural Antibodies in Chickens. *Clinical and Vaccine Immunology*. 13, 9975-9980.

Hermo, M.P., Saurina, J., Barbosa, J. and Barrón, D. (2014). High-resolution mass spectrometry applied to the study of metabolome modifications in various chicken tissues after amoxicillin administration. *Food Chemistry*, 153, 405-13.

Heywang, B.W., Thompson, C.R. and Kemmerer, A.R. (1959). Effect of Alfalfa Saponin on Laying Chickens. *Poultry Science*, 38, 968-971.

Isaacson, R. and Kim, H.B. (2012). The intestinal microbiome of the pig. *Animal Health Research Reviews*, 13, 100-109.

Ji, B., Ernest, B., Gooding, J.R., Das, S., Saxton, A.M., Simon, J., Dupont, J., Métayer-Coustard, S., Campagna, S.R. and Voy, B.H. (2012). Transcriptomic and metabolomic profiling of chicken adipose tissue in response to insulin neutralization and fasting. *BMC Genomics*, **13**, 441

Joyce, S.A., MacSharry, J., Casey, P.G., Kinsella, M., Murphy, E.F., Shanahan, F., Hill, C. and Gahan, C.G. (2014). Regulation of host weight gain and lipid metabolism by bacterial bile acid modification in the gut. Proceedings of the *National Academy of Sciences USA*, **111**, 7421-6.

Kamboh, A.A., Zhu, W.Y. (2013a). Individual and combined effects of genistein and hesperidin supplementation on meat quality in meat-type broiler chickens. *Journal of the Science of Food and Agriculture*, **93**, 3362-3367.

Kamboh, A.A., Zhu, W.Y. (2013b). Effect of Increasing Levels of Bioflavonoids in Broiler Feed on Plasma Anti-oxidative Potential, Lipid Metabolites and Fatty Acid Composition of Meat. *Poultry Science*, **92**, 454-461.

Kerr, A.K., Farrar, A.M., Waddell, L.A., Wilkins, W., Wilhelm, B. and Bucher, O. (2013). A systematic review-meta-analysis and meta-regression on the effect of selected competitive exclusion products on Salmonella spp. prevalence and concentration in broiler chickens. *Preventative Veterinary Medicine*, **05**. DOI: 10.1016/j.prevetmed.2013.04.005

Kim, H.B. and Isaacson, R.E. (2015). The pig gut microbial diversity: Understanding the pig gut microbial ecology through the next generation high throughput sequencing. *Veterinary Microbiology*, **12**, 177:242-251.

Kim, H.B., Sreevatsan, S., White, Singer, R.S. and Borewicz, K. (2012). Microbial shifts in the swine distal gut in response to the treatment with antimicrobial growth promoter, tylosin. *Proceedings of the National Academy of Sciences USA*, **109**(38), 15485-15490.

Kim, J., Nguyen, S.G., Guevarra, R.B., Lee, I. and Unno, T. (2015). Analysis of swine fecal microbiota at various growth stages. *Archives of Microbiology*, Apr 2. [Epub ahead of print]

La Ragione, R.M., Woodward, M.J., Kumar, M., Rodenberg, J., Fan, H., Wales, A.D. and Karaca, K. (2013). Efficacy of a live attenuated Escherichia coli O78:K80 vaccine in chickens and turkeys. *Avian Diseases*, **57**, 273-279.

Larsen, N., Finn, K.. Vogensen, F.K., van den Berg, F.W.J., Nielsen, D.S., Andreasen, A.S., Pedersen, B.K., Abu Al-Soud, W., Sørensen, S.J., Hansen, L.H. and Jakobsen, M. (2010) Gut microbiota in human adults with type 2 diabetes differs from non-diabetic adults PLOS Published: February 5, 2010 DOI: 10.1371/journal.pone.0009085

Lederberg, J. (2000). Infectious history. *Science*, **288**, 287-293.

Leser, T.D., Joanna, Z., Amenuvor, J.Z., Tim, K., Jensen, T.K., Rikke, H., Lindecrona, R.H., Mette Boye, M. and Møller, K. (2002). Culture-Independent Analysis of Gut Bacteria: the Pig Gastrointestinal Tract Microbiota Revisited. *Applied Environmental Microbiology*, **68**, 673-690.

Lewin, V. (1963). Reproduction and Development of Young in a Population of California Quail. *The Condo*, **65**, 249-278.

Lixandru, B., Drăcea, N., Dragomirescu, C., Drăgulescu, E., Coldea, I., Anton, L., Dobre, E., Rovinaru, C. and Codiţă, I. (2010). Antimicrobial activity of plant essential oils against bacterial and fungal species involved in food poisoning and/or food decay. *Roumanian archives of microbiology and immunology*, **69**, 224-230.

Lourenço, M.C., Kuritza, L.N., Hayashi, R.M., Miglino, L.B., Durau, J.F., Pickler, L. and Santin, E. (2015). Effect of a mannanoligosaccharide-supplemented diet on intestinal mucosa T lymphocyte populations in chickens challenged with Salmonella Enteritidis. *Journal of Applied Poultry Research*, **24**, 15-22.

Lumpkins, B.S., Batal, A.B. and Lee, M.D. (2010). Evaluation of the bacterial community and intestinal development of differentgenetic lines of chickens. *Poultry Science*, **89**, 1614-1621.

Lynch, D.B., Jeffery, I.B. and O'Toole, P.W. (2015). The role of the microbiota in ageing: current state and perspectives. *Interdisciplinary Reviews: Systems Biology and Medicine*, 7, 131-8.

Macfarlane, G.T. and Cummings, J.H. (1999). Probiotics and prebiotics: can regulating the activities of intestinal bacteria benefit health? *Western Journal of Medicine*, **171**, 187-191.

Mach, N., Berri, M., Estellé, J., Levenez, F., Lemonnier, G., Denis, C., Leplat, J.J., Chevaleyre, C., Billon, Y, Doré, J., Rogel-Gaillard, C. and Lepage, P. (2015). Early-life establishment of the swine gut microbiome and impact on host phenotypes. *Environmental Microbiology Reports*, 7, 554-69.

Mandal, S.M., Chakraborty, D. and Dey, S. (2010). Phenolic acids act as signaling molecules in plant-microbe symbioses. *Plant Signaling and Behaviour*, **5**, 359-368.

Mappley, L.J., Tchorzewska, M.A., Cooley, W.A., Woodward, M.J. and La Ragione, R.M. (2011). Lactobacilli antagonise growth, motility and adherence of Brachyspira pilosicoli: a potential intervention against avian intestinal spirochaetosis. *Applied Environmental Microbiology*, **15**, 77:5402-5411.

Mappley, L.J., Tchórzewska, M.A., Nunez, A., Woodward, M.J., Bramley, P.M. and La Ragione, R.M. (2013). Oral treatment of chickens with Lactobacillus reuteri LM1 reduces Brachyspira pilosicoli-induced pathology. *Journal of Medical Microbiology*, **62**(Pt 2), 287-96.

Martin, K.W. and Ernst, E. (2003). Antiviral agents from plants and herbs: a systematic review. *Antiviral Therapy*, **8**, 77-90.

Mazid, M., Khan, T. and Mohammad, F. (2011). Role of secondary metabolites in defence mechanisms of plants. *Free Radical Biology and Medicine*, **3**(2), 232-249.

McVey, A., Neufeld, K.A., Mao, Y.K., Bienenstock, J., Foster, J.A. and Kunze, W.A. (2013). The microbiome is essential for normal gut intrinsic primary afferent neuron excitability in the mouse. *Neurogastroenterology & Motility*. **25**(2), 183-e88.

Middleton, E., Kandaswami, C. and Theoharides, T.C. (2000). The effect of plant flavonoids on mammalian cells: Implications for inflammation, heart disease and cancer. *Pharmacological Reviews*, **52**, 673–751.

Missotten, J.A., Michiels, J., Degroote, J. and De Smet, S. (2015). Fermented liquid feed for pigs: an ancient technique for the future. *Journal of Animal Science and Biotechnology*, **20**, 6(1):4.

Muramatsu, T., Kodama, H., Morishita, T., Furuse, M. and Okumura, J. (1991). Effect of intestinal microflora on digestible energy and fiber digestion in chickens fed a high-fiber diet. *American Journal of Veterinary Research*, **52**, 1178-1181.

Muramatsu, T., Nakajima, S. and Okumura, J. (1994). Modification of energy metabolism by the presence of the gut microflora in the chicken. *British Journal of Nutrition*, **71**, 709-717.

Murphy, E.F., Cotter, P.D., Healy, S., Marques, T.M., O'Sullivan, O., Fouhy, F., Clarke, S.F., O'Toole, P.W., Quigley, E.M., Stanton, C., Ross, P.R., O'Doherty, R.M. and Shanahan, F. (2010). Composition and energy harvesting capacity of the gut microbiota: relationship to diet, obesity and time in mouse models. *Gut*, **59**, 1635-1642.

Osbourn, A., Goss, R. and Field, R. (2011). The saponins: polar isoprenoids with important and diverse biological activities. *National Product Reports*, **28**, 1261-1268.

Oso, A.O., Erinle, O.Y., William, G.A. and Ogunade, A.C. (2015). Interaction effect of whole wheat feeding and mannanoligosaccharides supplementation on growth performance, haematological indices and caecal microbiota of cockerel chicks. *Journal of Animal Physiology and Animal Nutrition*. doi: 10.1111/jpn.12314. [Epub ahead of print]

Pajarillo, E.A., Chae, J.P., Kim, H.B., Kim, I.H., Kang, D.K. (2015). Barcoded pyrosequencing-based metagenomic analysis of the faecal microbiome of three purebred piglines after cohabitation. *Applied Microbiology and Technology*, Feb 5. [Epub ahead of print]

Pan, D. and Yu, Z. (2014). Intestinal microbiome of poultry and its interaction with host and diet. *Gut Microbes*, **5**, 108-119.

Park, S.H., Hanning, I., Perrota, A., Bench, B.J., Alm, E. and Ricke, S.C. (2013). Modifying the gastrointestinal ecology in alternatively raised poultry and the potential for molecular and metabolomic assessment. *Poultry Science*, **92**, 546-561.

Pedersen, R., Andersen, A.D, Mølbak, L., Stagsted, J. and Mette Boye, B. (2013). Changes in the gut microbiota of cloned and non-cloned control pigs during development of obesity: gut microbiota during development of obesity in cloned pigs. *BMC Microbiology*, **13**, 30-42.

Pereira, D.I.A., Aslam, M..F, Frazer, D.M., Schmidt, A., Walton, G.E., McCartney, A.L., Gibson, G.R., Anderson, G.J. and Powell, J.J. (2015). Dietary iron depletion at weaning imprints low microbiome diversity and this is not recovered with oral nano Fe(III). *Microbiology Open*, **4**, 12–27.

Pieper, R., Neumann, K., Kröger, S., Richter, J.F., Wang, J., Martin, L., Bindelle, J., Htoo, J.K., Vahjen, V., Van Kessel, A.G. and Zentek, J. (2012). Influence of fermentable carbohydrates or protein on large intestinal and urinary metabolomic profiles in piglets. *Journal of Animal Science*, **90**(4), 34-36.

Podolak, I., Galanty, A. and Sobolewska, D. (2010). Saponins as cytotoxic agents: a review. *Phytochemistry Reviews*, **9**, 425-474.

Pulliainen, E. and Tunkkari, P. (1983). Seasonal changes in the gut length of the willow grouse (Lagopus Lagopus) in Finnish Lapland. *Annales Zoologici Fennici*, **20**, 53-56.

Qu, A., Brulc, J.M., Wilson, M.K., Law, B.F., Theoret, J.R., Joens, L.A., Konkel, M.E., Angly, F., Dinsdale, E.A., Edwards, R.A., Nelson, K.E. and White, B.R. (2008). Comparative Metagenomics Reveals Host Specific Metaviromes and Horizontal Gene Transfer Elements in the Chicken Cecum Microbiome. PLoS ONE 3(8):e2945. doi:10.1371/journal.pone.0002945

Rantala, M. and Nurmi, E. (1973). Prevention of the growth of Salmonella infantis in chicks by the flora of the alimentary tract of chickens. *British Poultry Science*, **14**, 627-30.

Roberfroid, M.B. (2000). Prebiotics and probiotics: are they functional foods? *American Journal of Clinical Nutrition*, **71**(6), 1682S–1687S.

Schokker, D., Zhang, J., Vastenhouw, S.A., Heilig, H.G., Smidt, H., Rebel, J.M. and Smits, M.A. (2015). Long-lasting effects of early-life antibiotic treatment and routine animal handling on gut microbiota composition and immune system in pigs. PLoS One. **6**:10(2):e0116523.

Searle, L.E.J., Best, A., Nunez, A., Johnson, L., Weyer, U., Dugdale, A.H., Cooley, W.A., Carter, B., Salguero, J., Tzortzis, G., Jones, G., Woodward, M.J. and La Ragione, R.M. (2009). A novel GOS mixture, Bimuno®, reduces Salmonella Typhimurium infection in mice. *Journal of Medical Microbiology*, 58, 37-48.

Searle, L.E.J., Cooley, W., Jones, G., Nunez, A., Crudgington, B., Weyer, U., Dugdale, A., Tzortzis, G., Collins, J., Woodward, M.J. and La Ragione, R.M. (2010) Purified galactooligosaccharide, derived from a mixture produced by the enzymic activity of bifidobacterium bifidum, reduces salmonella enterica serovar typhimurium adhesion and invasion *in vitro* and in vivo. *Journal of Medical Microbiology*, **59**, 1428-1439.

Sergeant, M.J., Constantinidou, C., Cogan, T.A., Bedford, M.R., Penn, C.W. and Pallen, M.J. (2014) Extensive Microbial and Functional Diversity within the Chicken Cecal Microbiome. PlosOne Published: March 21, 2014. doi: 10.1371/journal.pone.0091941.

Shim, S.B., Verstegen, M.W., Kim, I.H., Kwon, O.S. and Verdonk, J.M. (2005). Effects of feeding antibiotic-free creep feed supplemented with oligofructose, probiotics or synbiotics to suckling piglets increases the preweaning weight gain and composition of intestinal microbiota. *Archives of Animal Nutrition*, **59**, 419-427.

Slezak, K., Krupova, Z., Rabot, S., Loh, G., Levenez, F., Descamps, A., Lepage, P., Doré, J., Bellier, S., Blaut, M. (2014). Association of germ-free mice with a simplified human intestinal microbiota results in a shortened intestine. *Gut Microbes*, **5**, 176-82.

Soković, M., Glamočlija, J., Marin, P., Brkić, D., Van Griensven, L. (2010). Antibacterial effects of the essential oils of commonly consumed medicinal herbs using an *in vitro* model. *Molecules*, **15**, 7532-7546.

Spor, A., Koren, O. and Ley, R. (2011). Unravelling the effects of the environment and host genotype on the gut microbiome. *Nature Reviews Microbiology*, **9**, 279-290.

Stanley, D., Geier, M.S., Denman, S.E., Haring, V.R., Crowley, T.M., Hughes, R.J. and Moore, R.J. (2013). Identification of chicken intestinal microbiota correlated with the efficiency of energy extraction from feed. *Veterinary Microbiology*, **31**, 85-92.

Stockwell, C. (1988). *Nature's pharmacy.* Century Hutchinson Ltd. London, United Kingdom.

Straadt, I.K., Aaslyng, M.D. and Bertram, H.C. (2014). An NMR-based metabolomics study of pork from different crossbreeds and relation to sensory perception. *Meat Science*, **96**(2PtA), 719-728.

Tako, E., Glahn, G.P., Knez, M. and Stangoulis, J.C.R. (2014). The effect of wheat prebiotics on the gut bacterial population and iron status of iron deficient broiler chickens. *Nutrition Journal*, **13**, 58-67.

Tayel, A. and El-Tras, W. (2009) Possibility of fighting food borne bacteria by Egyptian folk medicinal herbs and spices extracts. *The Journal of the Egyptian Public Health Association*, **84**, 21-32.

Thi, P., Lan, N., Binh, T.L. and Benno, Y. (2003). Impact of two probiotic Lactobacillus strains feeding on faecal lactobacilli and weight gains in chicken. *Journal of General and Applied Microbiology*, **49**, 29-36

Thomson, W.A.R. ed (1978) *Medicines from the Earth*. McGraw-Hill Book Co: Maidenhead, UK.

Turnbaugh, P.J., Ley, R.E., Mahowald, M.A., Magrini, V., Mardis, E.R. and Gordon, J.I. (2006). An obesity-associated gut microbiome with increased capacity for energy harvest. *Nature*, **444**, 1027-1031

Umu, Ö.C., Frank, J.A., Fangel, J.U., Oostindjer, M., da Silva, C.S., Bolhuis, E.J., Bosch, G., Willats, W.G., Pope, P.B. and Diep, D.B. (2015). Resistant starch diet induces change in the swine microbiome and a predominance of beneficial bacterial populations. *Microbiome*, **3**, 16.

Van Dongen, W.F.D., White, J., Brandl, J., *et al.* (2013). Age-related differences in the cloacal microbiota of wild bird species. *BMC Ecology* 13: UNSP 11

Vinson, J., Su, X., Zubik, L. and Bose, P. (2001). Phenol antioxidant quantity and quality in foods: fruits. *Journal of Agricultural and Food Chemistry*, **49**(11), 5315-21

Vogt, S., Peña-Díaz, J. and Finlay, B.B. (2015). Chemical communication in the gut: Effects of microbiota-generated metabolites on gastrointestinal bacterial pathogens Anaerobe 05/2015; 34. doi: 10.1016/j.anaerobe.

Wei, S., Morrison, M. and Yu, Z. (2013). Bacterial census of poultry intestinal microbiome. *Poultry Science*, **92**, 671-683.

Werner, T., Wagner, S.J., Martínez, I., Walter, J., Chang, J.S., Clavel, T., Kisling, S., Schuemann, K. and Haller, D. (2011). Depletion of luminal iron alters the gut microbiota and prevents Crohn's disease-like ileitis. *Gut*, **60**, 325-33.

Wienemann, T., Schmitt-Wagner, D., Meuser, K., Segelbacher, G., Schink, B., Brune, A. and Berthold, P. (2011). The bacterial microbiota in the ceca of Capercaillie (Tetrao urogallus) differs between wild and captive birds. *Systematic and Applied Microbiology*, **34**, 542-551.

Yang, L., Bian, G., Su, Y. and Zhu, W. (2014). Comparison of faecal microbial community of lantang, bama, erhualian, meishan, xiaomeishan, duroc, landrace, and yorkshire sows. *Asian-Australasian Journal of Animal Science*, **27**, 898-906.

Zapata, H.J. and Quagliarello, V.J. (2015). The microbiota and microbiome in aging: potential implications in health and age-related diseases. *Journal of the American Geriatrics Society*, **63**, 776-81.

Zhao, W., Wang, Y., Liu, S., Huang, J., Zhai, Z., He, C., Ding, J., Wang, J., Wang, H., Fan, W., Zhao, J. and Meng, H. (2015). The dynamic distribution of porcine microbiota across different ages and gastrointestinal tract segments. PLoS One. 2015 Feb 17;10(2):e0117441. doi: 10.1371/journal.pone.0117441. eCollection 2015.

Zulkifli, I., Rahayu, H., Alimon, A., Vidyadaran, M. and Babjee, S. (2009). Gut microflora and intestinal morphology of commercial broiler chickens and red jungle fowl fed diets containing palm kernel meal. *Archiv für Geflügelkunde*, **73**, 49-55

8

Feeding A Growing Population: The Increasing Demand For High Quality Food

J. KENNEDY

PHD, Devenish Nutrition

According to the United Nations' World Population Prospects report[1], the world population is currently growing by approximately 74 million people per year. Having passed the 7 billion mark on October 31, 2011, the world population will, according to current United Nation predictions, reach 9.6 billion by 2050. Most of the population growth will occur in developing regions, which are projected to increase from 5.9 billion in 2013 to 8.2 billion in 2050. During the same period, the population of developed regions will remain largely unchanged at around 1.3 billion people.

While significant progress has been made over the last 20 years, persistent high levels of undernutrition—both hunger and micronutrient deficiencies, particularly in developing countries—remain. In addition, the burden of overweight and obesity is growing rapidly. These are all forms of malnutrition.

- The prevalence of hunger has declined from an estimated one billion people in 1990–92 to 805 million in 2012–14. That equates to a decrease in Global Hunger Index of 34 %. [2]Stunting (low height-for-age) and wasting (low weight-for-height) have also declined, both in numbers and in prevalence, but an estimated 161 million and 51 million children under five, respectively, were still affected in 2013.

- Micronutrient deficiencies, or "hidden hunger" due to a lack of vitamins and minerals in the diet, remain largely unchecked, affecting around 2 billion people (around 30 % of the world's population) with severe health consequences.

- Rates of obesity, in children and adults, have been rising rapidly, as has the incidence of non-communicable diseases related to diet, such as heart disease, stroke, cancer and diabetes. An estimated 42 million children under the age of five were overweight in 2013. More than 500 million adults are obese[3].

As the world population increases so too does the demand for high-value animal protein. Annual meat production is projected to increase from 218 million tonnes in 1997-1999 to 376 million tonnes by 2030. [4]Meat consumption in China more than doubled in 1980-2005, to 50kg a year per person. Between now and 2050, meat's share of calories will rise from 7% to 9%. [5]Global crop production needs to double by 2050. [6]Such demand leads to pressures on our natural resources; soil erosion, deforestation, water pollution and climate change.

There will be some gains in food production from taking in new land, using more irrigation or putting more fertiliser on existing fields, and cutting waste will make a difference. Other gains will come from; narrowing the gap between the worst and best producers; spreading the so-called "livestock revolution"; and taking advantage of new technologies. In terms of feed, the gains will come from optimising the genetic potential of animals through precision nutrition and improving feed conversion ratios.

However, the cost of food relative to earnings has never been as low as it is in Europe. In the UK, for example, food prices on average are about 10% of disposable household income, whereas 50 or 60 years ago they were roughly 25-30%. This is, in part due to the commoditization of food which represents a further challenge to the agri-food industry worldwide. However, continual efforts to reduce cost is a 'race to the bottom' that attracts food fraud and a reduction in quality that has human and animal health implications.

Feed represents over 70% of the input costs of intensively produced livestock. As producers seek to reduce input costs, nutrition can become sub-optimal with focus being placed solely on productivity rather than optimising life-time health status of livestock. The consequences of this may be hard to quantify in terms of animal production in the short-term as an animal will mobilise its own body reserves to make up the shortfall before performance begins to suffer. However the nutritional value of the produce from that animal will be compromised as will factors such as immune status. Genetic programs for livestock have disproportionately focussed on feed efficiency which demands that an animal produces more and more saleable product from less and less feed. The associated risk is that livestock receive sub-optimal nutrition especially in relation to micro-nutrition which impacts on both the eating quality and nutritional value of the food.

The value of meat for example can be increased by enhancing its nutritional value and creating a unique selling point. In the EU, Regulation 1924/2006 was published which concerns nutrition and health claims. The main aim of this regulation is to protect consumers from mis-leading claims by establishing a specific criteria for all nutrition and health claims on the EU market. For example, in order to make a nutrition claim on any food about Omega 3, it should contain 40mg EPA and DHA per 100g and 100kcal. This regulation brings huge value potential to the meat chain. A properly balanced diet for livestock will beneficially affect the animal, the consumer, the retailer and ultimately government by switching the emphasis from curing to preventing lifestyle related disease.

Staying with the Omega 3 example, two recent large prospective studies provide evidence of the benefits of elevated plasma levels of polyunsaturated fatty acids. The first describes a 30% reduction in total mortality, and a 40% reduction in coronary heart disease and stroke mortality in subjects with plasma Omega-3 levels in the highest quintile compared to those with plasma Omega-3 levels in the lowest quintile. The second paper found that subjects with plasma Omega-3 levels in the highest quartile had a 53% reduction in cardiovascular disease events (heart attacks and strokes) compared to those with plasma Omega-3 levels in the lowest quartile. The cost of CVD to the EU economy is estimated at €192 billion per year.

In summary, hunger and obesity represent opposite ends of the malnutrition spectrum and both represent a huge challenge to society. We need to increase food production but not at the expense of food quality.

[1] World Population Prospects: The 2012 Revision http://esa.un.org/wpp/

[2] Global Hunger Index The Challenge of hunger: Building resilience to achieve food and nutrition security

[3] Global nutrition policy review: hat does it take to scale up nutrition action? http://apps.who.int/iris/bitstream/10665/84408/1/9789241505529_eng.pdf

[4] Gardner, Brian. Global food futures: feeding the world in 2050. A&C Black, 2013.

[5] Alexandratos, Nikos, and Jelle Bruinsma. "World agriculture towards 2030/2050: the 2012 revision." ESA Work. Pap 3 (2012).

[6] Yield Trends Are Insufficient to Double Global Crop Production by 2050

9

Developments And Forecasts For Livestock Production In China

T. CHUNG WANG[1] AND M. VARLEY[2]

[1] Anyou International, Taicang, Shanghai, China,

[2] The Pig Technology Company

With a human population of 1.3 billion people, The People's Republic of China produced 87.07 million metric tonnes (MMT) of meat, 28.90 MMT of eggs, and 37.25 MMT of milk in 2014. The country therefore sustains a large volume of animal production in addition to importations.

Pig production in 2014 was 735 million head, and this was 2.75% more than in 2013. Pork production was 57.71 MMT, 3.2% more than 2013. Beef production was 6.89 MMT, and this was 2.4% more than in 2013. Lamb/mutton production was 4.28 MMT, 4.9% more than in 2013.

Poultry meat production was 17.51 MMT, a drop of 2.7% on 2013. The average pig farmer made a profit of 100 RMB (17 USD) per pig in August to October 2014, but in general lost money in the remainder of the year. With the background shadow of bird flu (avian influenza) around in 2014, it was not a good year for poultry meat producers. Layer feed supply dropped 4.4% in the year reflecting fewer eggs being produced in 2014. This made egg production very profitable in 2014, but the egg price started to drop in March 2015, when the new supply and demand balance was reached again.

Beef and milk production were still not meeting demand. Large volumes of beef and lamb were imported that kept the price low. Lamb/mutton prices have been good in the recent past, but this was not the case in 2014. The sharp 4.9% growth in supply made the price drop sharply.

After 20 years of very rapid growth, feed production volume is now starting to slow down. This is confirmed by the data presented in Tables 1 and 2. With the implementation of the new feed laws on 1st July 2012, and the slowing down in demand, the number of feed mills was down from 10,331 in 2013 to 5,531 at the end of 2014.

121

Table 1. Feed Production, 2014 vs. 2013, in MMT

	2014	vs. 2013
Compound feed	169.00	+3.80%
Protein concentrates	21.51	-10.00%
Vit/Min Premixes	6.41	+1.10%
Total	196.92	-0.40%

Table 2. Feed Production, 2014 vs. 2013, in MMT

	2014	vs. 2013
Pig	86.16	+2.40%
Layer (include ducks)	29.02	-4.40%
Broiler (with meat ducks)	50.33	+1.70%
Aqua	19.03	+2.10%
Ruminant	8.76	+10.20%
Others	3.97	+37.80%

Thus almost half of feed companies went out of business in 2014. There were 31 feed companies, 6 more than in 2013, producing more than 1 MMT per year in 2014. These 31 companies produced 103.52 MMT which was 52% of the total feed production. In other words the big companies became even bigger. China now has 9 (out of 23) provinces producing more than 10 MMT/year of feed. Almost all these provinces are along the Yangzi River and Pearl River where most people live. The Northeast, where most of the maize is produced, is also in the 10 MMT club.

The new member of this club is Jiangsu Province in the East of China. Feed that used to be produced in the Shanghai area has now moved into Jiangsu and Anhui provinces. The same applied to Beijing and Guangzhou cities. There ultimately will be no pigs allowed in these large cities. The slowing down in demand for feed made the country's feed production drop by 4% in the first quarter of 2015. The oversupply of pigs started at 2013. Less efficient pig farmers started losing money. Many of the smaller farms went out of business. After many years of fast growing feed companies, the industry slowed as a result. This same situation applies to poultry meat and egg production.

The message is very clear. China's high margin, fast growing animal production industry is coming to a turning point. This is also associated with new laws to deal with the country's food safety issues and environmental pollution issues. The goal is that all meat, milk and eggs on the table are produced from well regulated and manageable systems. This is not going to be easy, but one thing is for sure that the days of a few pigs in every back yard are gone. China's animal production industry is maturing. With today's government, this is going to happen very fast indeed.

The Forecast

The reasons for oversupply were legion but farmers were operating with more sows to compensate for the high mortality of piglets before 30 kg live weight. Efficiency also improved from 14 pigs/sow/year into the market to 16-17 pigs (still low by many international standards). Pigs were also slaughtered at a heavier weight, i.e. between 100 and 115 kg. This generated around 20% more of pork into the market. As a result, pig farmers lost money for about 18 months.

Pig farmers then started to reduce their sow numbers quickly. Some said China's sow herd dropped from its peak of 47 million at 2012 to 40 million at the end of 2014. The number of slaughter pigs and the sow population should start recovering from its record low in the first quarter of 2015. This is in line with the pig price starting to recover from lower than 12 RMB/kg (2 USD/kg) to 14 RMB/kg at mid May 2015. Pig feed production in the first quarter of 2015 dropped by 6.7%. Pig farmers should therefore make 100 RMB (17 USD)/pig profit again in the rest of 2015.

Pig producers moving up from small scale into larger industrial system should help the growth of pig feed production by 3-5% in the next 2-3 years. Production of egg layer feed increased by 3.4% in the first quarter of 2015. The balance of supply and demand for table eggs is reached again. This has also meant that it is a low margin time for egg producers again.

The gross margin for broiler producers was -3.8% in the first quarter of 2015. This was associated with broiler feed supply dropping to 11.43 MMT, a fall of 0.7%. Chinese consumers are willing to pay more for coloured birds than white birds. With the generally increased disposable income amongst consumers there is a demand for better quality food and more demand for feed for coloured birds may be seen again. This may be the only hope for the country's broiler production industry.

The effect of new farm regulations has also meant that ruminant p̶ ̶ ̶ ̶ ̶ ̶ ̶y moving into a more industrial scale feeding system. Ruminant feed production in the first quarter of 2015 was 3.78 MMT, i.e. 3.6% more than before. The first quarter's aquatic feeds production was 1.51 MMT. A growth of 8.1% compared to before. Amongst all species, aquatic production, and their feeds, have the highest margin and most potential for further growth in the next few years.

oth Maize and Soya Bean Meal (SBM) prices started to drop in Jan/Feb 2015. Based US soya production cost, the price for SBM in China may drop down to 2,700-2,600 MB/t (450-430 USD/t). Due to short supply, cotton seed meal and rape seed meal ices may not drop as much as SBM. SBM should be a bargain for feed producers in 15. Up to 15th of April 2015, the warehouses in the Northeast of China (i.e. main maize crop region), has stored 81.06 MMT of maize, which is 11 MMT more than 2014. The maize price for the rest of the year will be based on the volume of imported maize arriving at the sea ports, and if the government decide to take more maize into storage. China imported 19.51 MMT of grains in 2014, 33.8% more than 2013. China also imported 5.41 MMT of maize DDGS, 35.3% more than in 2013.

The feed industry used 11.19 MMT of imported sorghum/barley, and 15.00 MMT of imported wheat, to replace 26.19 MMT of maize in 2014. China also imported 2.27 MMT of sorghum, which is 4.5 times that in 2013 first quarter. The amount arriving in the second quarter of 2015 is estimated to be 3 MMT.

The amount of DDGS arriving was 0.39 MMT. The amount for the second quarter is estimated to be 1.8 MMT. The amount of barley imported in the first quarter was 2.66 MMT, a 71% increase. In the first quarter of 2015, the total volume of barley, sorghum and maize DDGS was 5.32 MMT; an 85% increase. The same things happened again in the second quarter of 2015. This made China seaports very busy. Feed mills in China now know how to utilise these new grains as replacements for maize.

Vitamin prices will stay low in general, but not Folic Acid and Vitamin B12. After one year's low prices for Lysine, Threonine and Tryptophan, the price should start to recover soon. Short supply for Methionine should stay the same for the rest of 2015.

Starting from February 2015, ingredient prices dropped by 5% on average. Feed prices dropped soon after that. Amongst all compound feeds, broiler feed price was the least profitable and the price dropped more than the others. Pork is still the main meat eaten on Chinese dinner tables. Even at a low level of 2015 local feed ingredients prices, cost for producing a pig in China is 2 times higher than that in the USA (Table 3). Pig farmers in the USA are making good money, but pig farmers in China only break even or are losing money.

Table 3. Maize and soyabean meal (SBM) prices, and pig production cost

2015	in China	in USA
Maize, in RMB(USD)/t	2,400 (40)	1,100-1,200 (<20)
SBM, in RMB(USD)/t	3,000 (50)	2,200 (37)
Pig cost, in RMB(USD)/kg	12-13 (2.0-2.2)	6-8 (1.0-1.3)

Conclusions

China is a very large country with a strong government and a fast growing economic environment. Business leaders now understand that with all the changes in this financial and operating environment, being 'big and strong' is no longer the only golden rule to success. This applies not only to the prices consumers are now paying, but also more attention is given to food safety, quality, services, and even to animal production's effect on the environment.

Producers now understand that their company's image and reputation is more important than the results shown in financial reports. To stay successfully in business, cutting production cost is not the only way right now. The government's new laws to deal with supplying food safety and a low level of environmental pollution issues became a heavy cost to the production system.

Many feed mills have been forced to close down simply because of inability to meet the basic requirements. To stay in this new business environment, change must be made, or you will be forced out of the industry. In making this transition, some businesses decided to re-model or re-build their enterprise. For example, putting money into basic research, building a strong services team, standardized protocols to improve efficiency, introduce e-commerce, using big data analysis, and simulation. Making these changes needs investment money to support the changes. We all know that consumers cannot do without meat, milk and eggs. The general public are willing to buy stocks of companies in animal production businesses. Going the 'Initial Public Offering' (IPO) route is a good way of getting the necessary funding, and many companies have already taken this course of action. Many things of this kind are now taking place in China and opportunities are still there. It is not clear what will happen in 5 years' time but one thing is certain. Those companies that do not change will not be there in 5 years' time.

Acknowledgment

Market information, and official data provided by Beijing Boyar Communication Co. Ltd.

10

N-3 Fatty Acids And Reproduction In The Pig

J.A. ROOKE

Future Farming Systems, SRUC, West Mains Road, Edinburgh EH9 3JG.

Introduction

Sow productivity is comprised of various components that determine the number of piglets attaining slaughter weight per year. In the UK, the importance of sow productivity has been given focus by the BPEX "Breed+3" initiative which aims to help every producer produce an extra three pigs per sow per year. This is approximately the difference in performance between the average and top-third of UK producers (Table 1, Agriculture and Horticulture Development Board, 2014) in piglets reared per sow per year. This difference between the segments of the industry is not a result of any single factor but a combination of differences in fertility, litter size at birth and piglet mortality. There is therefore scope for improvement in all aspects of reproductive performance. Correct nutrition of the sow and to a lesser extent the boar has a major effect on reproductive success. Recently there has been increasing interest in the role of n-3 fatty acids and potential benefits for reproductive performance. In this chapter recent studies using n-3 fatty acids are reviewed and their implication for future work discussed.

Table 1. UK Breeding herd performance 2013 (AHDB 2014)

Sector	Average	Top –third
Successful services (%)	83.2	87.0
Litters / year	2.29	2.35
Total piglets born	12.5	13.4
Mortality (%)	13.1	11.2
Number piglets reared		
/litter	10.3	11.2
/year	23.5	26

Fatty acids

Apart from the overall importance of dietary fat as a source of energy, nutritionally, oils and other fat-containing feeds are important as sources of essential fatty acids.

The structure of fatty acids will be described using the following nomenclature with linoleic acid (LA), 18:2 n-6, as an example where: 18 left of the colon denotes the number of carbon atoms in the fatty acid; 2 to the right of the colon, the number of double bonds in the carbon chain and n-6, the position of the first double bond counting from the methyl end of the carbon chain. The essentiality of fatty acids in mammalian nutrition is determined by the absence of the desaturase enzymes necessary to introduce double bonds between the methyl end of the fatty acid carbon chain and the n-9 position. There are two functionally important series of essential polyunsaturated fatty acids (PUFA) which contain their first double bond at either the n-3 or n-6 positions: the 18 carbon fatty acids, LA and 18:3 n-3 (linolenic acid, LNA) are the parent compounds from which all other metabolically important fatty acids are synthesised. The biological importance of the essential fatty acids resides in the longer chain PUFA that are synthesised from the 18 carbon fatty acids.

Biosynthesis of fatty acids

The structure and common names of the essential fatty acids and their biosynthetic routes are given in Figure 1. The key points to note from Figure 1 are:

- Both LA and LNA are substrates for the same desaturase and elongase enzymes that synthesise longer chain PUFA.

- n-3 and n-6 fatty acids cannot be inter-converted.

- the rate limiting step in the pathway is the first desaturation step catalysed by delta 6 desaturase.

- The final desaturation step in synthesis of docosahexaenoic acid (22:6 n-3, DHA) is catalysed by the same delta 6 desaturase enzyme that desaturates 18 carbon PUFA.

The entire pathway described by Sprecher (2000) is active in piglet liver at 14 days of age (Li, Kaplan and Hachey, 2000). However, no synthesis of DHA from eicosapentaenoic acid (20:5 n-3, EPA) could be detected in foetal piglet liver. Expression of the delta 5 and 6 desaturase enzymes in piglet liver is low at birth although expression increases between birth and 28 days of age (De Quelen, Boudry and Mourot, 2013). Therefore, the capacity of the foetal and neonatal piglet for synthesis of long chain PUFA is limited.

Essential fatty acid requirements

Nutrient requirements recommendations for fatty acids (National Research Council, 2012) express requirements for n-6 PUFA as LA but while acknowledging the essentiality of n-3 PUFA, do not give a requirement as it is assumed that normal diets

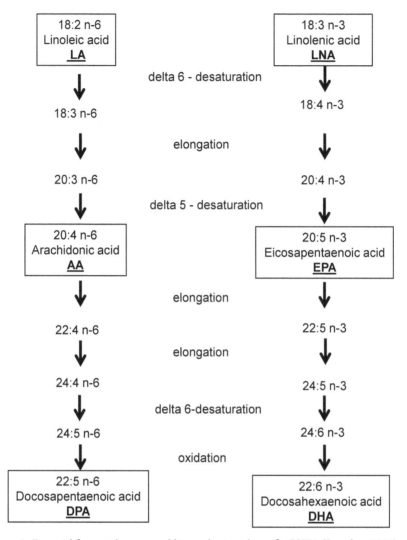

Figure 1. Essential fatty acid names and biosynthetic pathway for PUFA (Sprecher, 2000).

will provide an adequate supply. This is in contrast to human nutrition (Food and Agricultural Organisation of the United Nations 2010) where the minimum intakes (% of dietary energy) required to prevent deficiency have been defined as 2.5% for LA and 0.5% for LNA. For a healthy diet, a total PUFA intake (n-6 and n-3 fatty acids) of between 6 and 11% of dietary energy is suggested. Specific daily intakes have also been recommended for EPA plus DHA of 250 mg/day which are increased during pregnancy and lactation to at least 300 mg/day of which 200 mg/day should be DHA. This recognises the conditional essentiality of DHA during pregnancy to ensure adequate supplies of DHA for the developing foetus. If intakes of n-6 and n-3 fatty acids are within the range of total recommended intake (6 to 11 % dietary energy) it was also concluded that there was no need to specify an optimum ratio of n-6 to n-3 PUFA in the diet.

Sources of PUFA

Current diets for pregnant and lactating sows, being based on cereals and by-products derived from cereals and oilseeds, normally contain proportionately more n-6 than n-3 fatty acids and little or no EPA and DHA. As can be seen in Table 2, n-3 fatty acid sources are restricted mainly to linseed (flaxseed) oil for LNA. Marine oils are the primary sources of EPA and DHA and there is considerable variation in relative amounts of EPA and DHA. The starting point for considering effects of n-3 fatty acids on reproduction in the pig is that current diets may supply sub-optimal amounts of n-3 fatty acids.

Table 2. Typical linoleic (LA) and linolenic (LNA) contents (g/100g total fatty acids) of common vegetable oils (Nettleton 1995)

	LA	LNA
Linseed	16	58
Maize	61	1
Rapeseed	26	10
Soya bean	54	7
Sunflower	69	-

Functions of PUFA

At the cellular and molecular level, there are several mechanisms through which PUFA may mediate their effects. As PUFA are components of the phospholipids of the cell membrane, specific membranes have a PUFA composition that is optimum for the function of proteins within the membrane. In the pig, in common with most mammals, the lipids of brain, retina and spermatozoa contain substantially higher proportions of DHA than other tissues. The DHA acyl side chains in cell membranes containing DHA-rich phospholipids are highly flexible and able to convert rapidly from an extended to a looped conformation. This endows these membranes with high levels of flexibility, compressibility and elasticity which allow the membranes to accommodate changes in conformation important for the function of, for example, rhodopsin, the pigment in the retina whose photo-activation is the first step in light detection. Other protein-protein and protein-lipid interactions are facilitated by DHA containing phospholipids and these mechanisms may explain the importance of DHA in neural transmission.

A principal function of arachidonic acid (20:4 n-6, AA) is as a substrate for synthesis of prostaglandins and other eicosanoid mediators whose major function is to modulate intensity of the inflammatory reaction (Calder, 2002). Prostaglandins and other eicosanoids are synthesised from phospholipid-bound AA by cycloxygenase and lipoxygenase after AA release from phospholipids principally by phospholipase A_2 (Figure 2). The prostaglandin products from AA are 2 series prostaglandins which include prostaglandins $F_{2\alpha}$ and E_2. As in biosynthesis of PUFA, n-3 fatty acids, particularly EPA are also substrates for the enzymes involved in biosynthesis of prostaglandins but produce 3 series prostaglandins which are considered to be less biologically active than 2 series prostaglandins. In addition, feeding EPA decreases the amounts of AA in membranes and EPA also inhibits phospholipase A_2 mediated release of AA from phospholipids and competitively inhibits the activity of cycloxygenase and lipoxygenase. The net effect of feeding EPA is therefore to reduce effects of AA mediated prostaglandin production and n-3 PUFA are therefore EPA is considered to be anti-inflammatory. Although DHA is a poor substrate for cyclooxygenase, it has recently been found that DHA-derived bioactive D-series resolvins and protectins have potent anti-inflammatory activity.

Fatty acids are not only components of biological membranes and substrates for eicosanoid production but also involved in modification of gene expression. PUFA down regulate genes involved in both lipogenesis and glycolysis. PUFA exert these effects on gene expression by regulating three major transcriptional factors controlling multiple pathways involved in lipid metabolism. PUFA activate

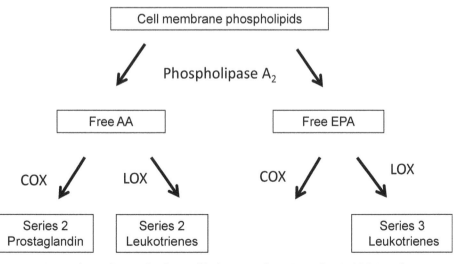

Figure 2. Biosynthesis of prostaglandins and leukotrienes from AA and EPA. (COX, cycloxygenase; LOX lipoxygenase.

peroxisome proliferator activated receptor and suppress the nuclear abundance of carbohydrate regulatory element binding protein and sterol regulatory element binding protein. PUFA activation of peroxisome proliferator activated receptor enhances fatty acid oxidation, while suppression of sterol regulatory element binding protein and carbohydrate regulatory element binding protein results in inhibition of de novo synthesis of fatty acids.

Study selection

To assess progress since this area was last discussed (Rooke, Ferguson, Sinclair and Speake, 2003), the subsequent literature was searched. In general the criteria of Sargeant, Rajic, Read and Ohlsson (2006) were used to select studies: an adequate description of treatments imposed; inclusion of a suitable control; use of a large enough sample size; appropriate statistical methods; avoidance of data repetition (e.g. where components of a single study are reported in several papers); and exclusion of conference abstracts / proceedings. In respect of this review, issues of concern were:

- An adequate treatment description: studies in which dietary fatty acid concentrations were not reported are difficult to interpret.

- Controls in which fat sources were added as a supplement are similarly difficult to interpret as changes in fatty acid composition are confounded by increasing amounts of fat.

- Sample size is important: where the response is a litter characteristic such as survival and data are not normally distributed then sample size required is greater than the minimum of five noted by Sargeant *et al.* (2006).

The literature since 2000 was searched and 39 references found which related to sows and n-3 fatty acids. Of these references, 3 were reviews which were discarded; 10 were incidences of data repetition; 3 contained less than 5 observations per treatment. Closer examination of the 23 remaining studies revealed that 5 did not include production data (but provided useful mechanistic information), 5 did not include dietary fatty acid composition (but included potentially useful production information) leaving 13 studies which met all criteria. Within these 13 studies, there was considerable heterogeneity. Only in 5 studies (4 from day 107 of gestation to weaning and 1 throughout pregnancy to day 107) matched usual commercial practice. The n-3 fatty sources were linseed (6), fish (5) or linseed and fish oils included within the same study (2) and control diets included palm (4), tallow or lard (6), sunflower (4) or maize oils (2).

Responses to n-3 fatty acids

Given the wide variation in experimental designs employed in these studies in order to meet experiment-specific objectives, it is not surprising that when Tanghe and De Smet (2013) reviewed the literature to 2011 they concluded that although responses were not consistent, most studies found no effect on litter size but there were indications of some positive effects on piglet vitality and growth. Including studies published since 2011, overall there is no reason to disagree with Tanghe and De Smet (2013). However, recent studies do shed new light on the area and these will provide the focus for the remainder of this review.

Responses in sperm quality

Boar spermatozoa in common with other mammalian sperm contain phospholipids with very high concentrations of the 22 carbon fatty acids, DHA and DPA, (Leskanich and Noble 1999). It is thought that the proportions of DHA and DPA are reciprocally related and the presence of DPA probably reflects either a sub-optimal supply to or synthesis of DHA within the testis. A decrease in the ratio of DHA to DPA is associated both with increases in boar age (Speake, Surai and Rooke, 2003) and increased proportions of spermatozoa with both reduced motility and viability (Strzezek, Fraser, Kuklinska, Dziekonska and Lecewicz, 2004; Am-In, Kirkwood, Techakumphu and Tantasuparuk, 2011). Although, positive responses to supplementation of the diet with long chain n-3 PUFA have been noted (Strzezek *et al.*, 2004) which were broadly similar to Rooke *et al*, (2003), recently Castellano, Audet, Bailey, Chouinard, Laforest and Matte (2010) reported no response to fish oil supplementation. One factor which could explain the variability of responses may be the genotype of the boar as Yeste, Barrera, Coll and Bonet (2011) found that whereas fish oil supplementation increased proportions of mature sperm in Large White and Pietrain boars no response was observed in Duroc boars. Interestingly there has been no report of effects of feeding linseed oil to boars.

Ovulation, fertilisation and implantation

Because ovulation occurs shortly after weaning in the sow, a proportion of oocyte development takes place during lactation. Therefore direct effects of the lactation diet on oocyte quality and carry over effects on ovulation and subsequent implantation will be confounded to some extent by the development of the current litter. Therefore gilts have been used to assess effects of n-3 fatty acids on events up to and including implantation. Perez Rigau, Lindemann, Kornegay, Harper and Watkins (1995) added 40 g/kg of either coconut oil (medium chain fatty acids), soya-bean oil (mainly LA) or Menhaden fish oil (EPA and DHA) to the diet of gilts prior to service and continued until slaughter between days 37 to 45 post-service. Overall, Menhaden oil improved the number of live foetuses (68%, as a percentage of the numbers of corpora lutea) when compared to a starch-based isoenergetic control diet (63%); results were variable and responses were less marked in multiparous sows than in gilts. Similarly, Smits, Luxford, Mitchell and Nottle (2013) added 3 or 10 g fish oil / kg to the diet of gilts from approximately 40 days prior to and for 25 days after mating and noted an increase in embryo survival with fish oil. However, Brazle, Johnson, Webel, Rathbun and Davis (2009) found no response in embryo number at 19 days post oestrous.

Litter effects in current generation

In the previous review, Rooke *et al.*, (2003) concluded, largely based on the authors' own studies, that responses to n-3 PUFA were largely positive and it appeared that inclusion of long chain PUFA in the diet was necessary. This contrasts with Tanghe and De Smet (2013) who found inconsistent responses to feeding the sow n-3 PUFA. Several suggestions for future research posed by Rooke *et al.* (2003) are also worth addressing.

- The efficiency of incorporation of dietary LNA fed during pregnancy into long chain n-3 PUFA in piglet tissues was about 0.20 of the response gained from feeding equivalent amounts of DHA and EPA. Whether feeding increased amounts of LNA could substitute for feeding DHA and EPA has not been evaluated.

- The relative amounts of EPA and DHA differs between fish oils. Nutritionally this may be important as some negative responses have been attributed to EPA content of fish oils.

- There was a scarcity of trials involving large numbers of sows.

Since the review of Tanghe and De Smet (2013) several studies have dealt with the above issues. Recent progress will be assessed from these reports particularly in the context of concerns about the sustainability of fish oil supply (Millet and Delezie, 2013), the competition of the fish farming industry for fish oil worldwide, and the presence of contaminants such as heavy metals, dioxins and PCB in marine oils (Tocher, 2009).

Responses to different n-3 PUFA

Piglet tissue fatty acid composition

Rooke, Shanks and Edwards (2000) concluded that LNA was relatively ineffective in modifying neonatal piglet tissue DHA: LNA increased brain DHA 0.17 fold values obtained with supplying DHA in fish oil, leading to the conclusion that marine oils were the preferred route for increasing piglet EPA and DHA. Tanghe, Millet and De Smet (2013) recently compared linseed, echium and fish oils (10 g oil / kg diet from day 73 of pregnancy to weaning). Echium oil is a source of 18:4 n-3, the product of delta 6 desaturation of LNA and it was hypothesised that echium oil would be more effective than linseed oil given that delta 6 desaturase is the rate-limiting enzyme in the biosynthetic pathway for PUFA. In fact responses to echium oil did not differ from those to linseed oil and so will not be discussed further. In piglet plasma sampled at birth, feeding linseed oil did increase plasma EPA and DHA but to a lesser extent than feeding fish oil (EPA 0.38 and DHA 0.24 of fish oil response). Farmer and Petit (2009) fed 35 g linseed oil / kg diet from day 63 of gestation to weaning and also found significant increases in piglet brain DHA due to feeding linseed oil. The effect of increasing amounts of LNA (0, 10 and 40 g linseed /kg from day 28 of pregnancy) were assessed by De Quelen, Boudry and Mourot (2010) from newborn piglet liver and brain composition. Liver EPA was increased in a dose dependant manner but, whereas liver and brain DHA were increased by feeding 10g/kg linseed oil, there was no benefit from feeding 40 g/kg linseed oil. Finally, Eastwood, Leterme and Beaulieu (2014) varied amounts of linseed or fish oils fed in diets containing 50 g crude fat / kg diet from day 80 of pregnancy to weaning to supply the same amount of n-3 PUFA (4.8 g/kg diet) and additionally linseed oil to supply 14 g n-3 PUFA / kg diet. Compared to a maize oil control diet increases in piglet serum EPA were 0.04 and 0.10 of fish oil responses for the low and high levels of linseed oil inclusion, and linseed oil did not increase serum DHA. Thus, if the utility of feeding linseed oil during gestation is judged from its ability to increase piglet EPA and DHA, then it is less effective than fish oil. However, although there was substantial variation between studies, linseed oil did increase piglet EPA and DHA status at birth, and these responses were maintained until weaning (Tanghe *et al*,. 2013), the question arises as to whether there were also responses in performance to feeding linseed oil.

Piglet responses to linseed or fish oils

Tanghe *et al.* (2013) found that piglets born to sows fed on linseed oil had greater birth-weights (1.54 vs 1.41 kg) and grew faster to weaning (240 v 214 g/d) than those born to sows fed on fish oil. Farmer, Giguere and Lessard (2010) found no advantage in litter size or birth or weaning-weights when linseed oil was fed, but when linseed oil was fed there were reductions in piglet mortality (%)at days 2 (24.5 v 20.1) and 21 (27.1 vs 22.2) after birth. Eastwood *et al*, (2014) found that although weaning weights for sows fed a lesser amount of linseed (8.6 kg) were similar to controls (8.6 kg), weaning weights were reduced for fish oil (7.8 kg) and a higher inclusion of linseed (8.0 kg). In a comprehensive study reported by Tanghe, Missotten, Raes, Vangeyte and De Smet (2014a), large groups of sows (47 to 91) were fed either linseed or fish oil alone or in combination (see Table 3 for design) from day 45 of gestation to weaning. Sows fed linseed oil only, on average had 0.9 more live-born piglets and weaned 0.5 more piglets than sows fed diets containing fish oil. Although there was no difference between treatments in birth–weight, at 5 and 21 days of age, piglet and litter weights were greater when linseed rather than fish oil was included in the diets. As there was no dose-dependant response, differences between treatments were due to differences in fatty composition of the diets fed. Thus overall in these recent studies, feeding linseed oil rather than fish oil supported superior performance both in the current and subsequent gestation.

Table 3. Dietary treatments and litter size and piglet weaning weights adapted from Tanghe *et al.* (2014a)

Treatment	Litter size	Piglet weight day 21
Control (palm oil)	11.7	5.9
Linseed (5 g/kg)		
Linseed (20 g/kg)	12.0	6.2
Fish (5 g/kg)		
Fish (20 g/kg)	11.1	5.8
Linseed (5 g/kg) plus Fish (5g/kg)		
Linseed (5 g/kg) plus Fish (20 g/kg)	12.1	5.3

Means given for overall effects of linseed, fish or linseed plus fish treatments as no effects of level of oil inclusion

Litter size responses in subsequent generation

When treatments including n-3 PUFA were terminated at weaning and performance in the subsequent gestation recorded, Smits, Luxford, Mitchell and Nottle (2011) recorded an increase in litter size when 3.3 g fish oil / kg diet was fed (Table 4). Tanghe *et al.* (2014a) found that diets containing linseed and fish oils supported more live-born piglets than palm oil–fed control sows; notably linseed oil was superior to fish oil (Table 4). Eastwood *et al.* (2014) also found effects on sow performance in the generation subsequent to feeding linseed or fish oil during gestation and lactation: although pre-weaning mortality was increased when linseed or fish oil was fed, fish-oil fed sows had lower birth and weaning weights than linseed oil-fed sows. Thus although feeding n-3 PUFA increased litter size in these studies, linseed performed better than fish oil.

Table 4. Effect of feeding n-3 fatty acids until weaning on litter size (piglets born alive) in the next generation

Study	Control	Linseed oil	Fish oil	Linseed plus Fish oils
Eastwood *et al.* (2014)	14	12.9	14.4	
Smits *et al.,* (2011)	9.3		10.3	
Tanghe *et al.,* (2014a)	10.8	12.4	11.0	11.8

The mechanisms underlying the differences in performance above between linseed and fish oils are unclear. In part, the superiority of linseed oil may arise from sensitivity of the oocyte to oxidative damage. First, the fatty acid composition of the oocyte contains substantial quantities of saturated fatty acids (Prates, Alves, Marques, Baptista, Horta, Bessa and Pereira, 2013) and increased amounts of PUFA in the oocyte may be deleterious to oocyte development (Sturmey, Reis, Leese and McEvoy, 2009). Linseed oil will pose a lesser oxidative challenge to oocytes as it contains LNA rather than the EPA and DHA in fish oils. Secondly, Eastwood *et al.* (2014) proposed that differences in mortality they recorded may have been due to reduced production of the luteolytic prostaglandin $PGF_{2\alpha}$ as did Tanghe *et al.* (2014a) who also suggested that while piglet tissue AA was reduced when fish oil was fed, the effect was less or absent when linseed oil was fed. Thirdly, another contributory factor may have been the EPA content of the fish oils fed. This may be important as reduced infant growth has been attributed to high EPA contents of fish oils (Carlson, Werkman, Peeples, Cooke and Tolley, 1993). In the studies of Tanghe *et al.* (2014a) and Eastwood *et al.* (2014), ratios of DHA to EPA in the fish oil–containing diets were 0.6 and 0.7 respectively (see Table 5).

Table 5. Amounts of EPA and DHA and their ratio in different experiments

Study	Oil source	EPA	DHA	DHA:EPA
Eastwood *et al.* (2014)				
(g/kg diet)	Herring	1.65	1.03	0.62
Smits *et al.* (2011)				
(g/kg dietary fatty acids)	Salmon	2.4	4.0	1.67
Tanghe *et al.* (2014a)				
(g/kg dietary fatty acids)	Fish	6.20	4.27	0.69
Rooke et al (2001a)				
(g/kg dietary fatty acids)	Tuna orbital	3.9	17.6	4.97
Rooke et al (2001b)				
(g/kg dietary fatty acids)	Salmon	1.5	2.3	1.53

This contrasts with higher values of 5.0 (Rooke, Sinclair and Edwards, 2001a), 1.5 (Rooke, Sinclair and Ewen, 2001b) and 1.7 (Smits *et al.*, 2011) where positive responses to feeding tuna and salmon oils respectively were reported. EPA may be mediating effects by displacing AA from membranes or by competition for eicosanoid biosynthesis. Indeed an inclusion rate of 10 g salmon oil /kg diet (Rooke *et al.*, 2003) was recommended as it increased piglet tissue DHA with the minimum reduction of AA.

Responses to algal biomass

If the EPA content of fish oils is responsible for inferior performance to linseed oil, then specific algal oils or biomass can provide alternative sources specifically of DHA without EPA and other fatty acids. In sheep, Pickard, Beard, Seal and Edwards (2008) found that algal DHA improved lamb vigour, and Gabler, Spencer, Webel and Spurlock (2007) reported improved intestinal glucose absorption and muscle glycogen stores in weaned piglets whose dams had been fed algal DHA throughout gestation and lactation. Adeleye, Brett, Blomfield, Guy and Edwards (2014) fed algal biomass to supply 0.3 and 3 g DHA / kg diet from day 87 of gestation until weaning. DHA-feeding reduced stillbirths and increased piglet vitality at birth (as measured by latency to stand, find a teat and suckle). However, weaning weights were reduced when 3 g DHA / kg was fed. It is possible that retro-conversion of DHA to EPA may have been responsible for reductions in growth of piglets to weaning as Gabler *et al.* (2007) reported that algal DHA increased EPA concentrations in sow milk and piglet muscle. Increases in piglet vitality in response to feeding n-3 PUFA have been reported in some (Rooke *et al.*, 2001b) but not all (Tanghe *et al.*, 2014a) studies.

Low birth-weight piglet responses

If increases in n-3 fatty acid supply to the sow are responsible for improvements in piglet vitality then it is possible that low birth-weight piglets which are most at risk of neonatal morbidity and mortality may benefit more than average size piglets. Tanghe, Millet, Missotten, Vlaeminck and De Smet (2014b) indeed found that low birth-weight piglets had lower brain DHA content than their heaviest litter mates; however, including n-3 PUFA in the maternal diet did not favour the low birth-weight piglets. Similarly, (Laws, Litten, Laws, Lean, Dodds and Clarke, 2009) found only small differences in performance between low birth-weight piglets fed fish and other oils. Finally, Smit, Spencer, Patterson, Dyck, Dixon and Foxcroft (2015) found that fish oil only improved growth rate in litters selected for average rather than low birth-weight phenotypes. Thus any effects of n-3 PUFA do not seem to preferably favour the low birth–weight at risk piglets.

Other effects of n-3 fatty acids

A series of studies have reported effects of feeding n-3 PUFA during gestation and lactation on aspects of piglet immune and intestinal functions and brain structure. It is difficult to draw overall conclusions given the wide range of outcomes measured. For immune function, Luo, Huang, Xiao, Chen, Jiang and Peng (2009) interpreted changes in piglet T helper cell proliferation in response to fish oil as indicating improved immune maturation; Farmer et al. (2010) concluded there were beneficial effects on immune resistance when linseed was included in the diet of sows in various forms but attributed the response to feeding linseed rather than linseed oil specifically. Leonard, Sweeney, Bahar, Lynch and O'Doherty (2010) reported that in response to fish oil weaned piglets had an increased phagocytic response to E. coli, but Tanghe, Cox, Melkebeek, De Smet and Millet (2014c) reported no major effect of linseed or fish oil feeding on adaptive immunity. In relation to intestinal function, Boudry, Douard, Mourot, Lalles and Le Huerou-Luron (2009) interpreted changes in mast cell degranulation in piglets when linseed oil was fed to sows to show that these piglets were less sensitive to stress, whereas using the same dietary model, De Quelen, Chevalier, Rolli-Derkinderen, Mourot, Neunlist and Boudry (2011) reported changes in intestinal permeability. In addition to changes in intestinal glucose uptake noted above with algal biomass, inclusion of fish oil in the maternal diet also improved glucose uptake (Gabler et al. 2007; Gabler, Radcliffe, Spencer, Webel and Spurlock, 2009). Finally, Vallet, Rempel, Miles and Webel (2014) quantified piglet brain myelination and found that it was improved by feeding the sow fish oil. Thus overall a variety of indices have in general been improved by n-3 fatty acid supplementation of the gestation and lactation diet; however in most cases study size limited the ability to relate these changes to production-relevant outcomes.

Conclusions

In response to the question, "Do n-3 fatty acids improve reproductive performance in the pig?", overall the conclusion must be in agreement with Tanghe and De Smet (2013) that production responses are variable but there are positive indications. Recent studies which have compared linseed and fish oils, have found superior responses to linseed over fish oils, particularly in growth to weaning and subsequent litter size. This may in part be caused by the EPA content of fish oils. Future work should focus on

- Are there responses in boar fertility to feeding linseed oil as a source of LNA?

- Use of DHA algal biomass to establish whether it is the EPA content of fish oils that is responsible for the benefits seen with linseed oil

- Long term feeding studies to establish whether increases in litter size in response to feeding both linseed and fish oils persist for more than one generation.

Acknowledgments

SRUC receives funding from Scottish Government's Rural and Environmental Science and Analytical Services Division.

References

Adeleye, O., Brett, M., Blomfield, D., Guy, J. and Edwards S. (2014) The effect of algal biomass supplementation in maternal diets on piglet survival in two housing systems. *Livestock Science*, **162**, 193-200.

Agriculture and Horticulture Development Board (2014) *The BPEX Yearbook 2013-2014*. Agriculture and Horticulture Development Board, Kenilworth, UK.

Am-In, N., Kirkwood, R., Techakumphu, M. and Tantasuparuk, W. (2011) Lipid profiles of sperm and seminal plasma from boars having normal or low sperm motility. *Theriogenology*, **75**, 897-903.

Boudry, G., Douard, V., Mourot, J., Lalles, J.P. and Le Huerou-Luron I. (2009) Linseed oil in the maternal diet during gestation and lactation modifies fatty acid composition, mucosal architecture, and mast cell regulation of the ileal barrier in piglets. *Journal of Nutrition*, **139**, 1110-1117.

Brazle, A.E., Johnson, B.J., Webel, S.K., Rathbun, T.J. and Davis D.L. (2009) Omega-3 fatty acids in the gravid pig uterus as affected by maternal supplementation with omega-3 fatty acids. *Journal of Animal Science*, **87**, 994-1002.

Calder, P.C. (2002) Dietary modification of inflammation with lipids. *Proceedings of the Nutrition Society*, **61**, 345-358.

Carlson, S.E., Werkman, S.H., Peeples, J.M., Cooke R.J. and Tolley E.A. (1993) Arachidonic-acid status correlates with 1st year growth in preterm infants. *Proceedings of the National Academy of Sciences of the United States of America*, **90**, 1073-1077.

Castellano, C., Audet, I., Bailey, J., Chouinard, P., Laforest, J. and Matte, J. (2010) Effect of dietary n-3 fatty acids (fish oils) on boar reproduction and semen quality. *Journal of Animal Science*, **88**, 2346-2355.

De Quelen, F., Boudry, G. and Mourot, J. (2010). Linseed oil in the maternal diet increases long chain-PUFA status of the foetus and the newborn during the suckling period in pigs. *British Journal of Nutrition*, **104**, 533-543.

De Quelen, F., Chevalier, J., Rolli-Derkinderen, M., Mourot, J., Neunlist, M. and Boudry, G. (2011) n-3 polyunsaturated fatty acids in the maternal diet modify the postnatal development of nervous regulation of intestinal permeability in piglets. *Journal of Physiology-London*, **589**, 4341-4352.

De Quelen, F., Boudry, G. and Mourot, J. (2013) Effect of different contents of extruded linseed in the sow diet on piglet fatty acid composition and hepatic desaturase expression during the post-natal period. *Animal*, **7**, 1671-1680.

Eastwood, L., Leterme, P. and Beaulieu, A. (2014) Changing the omega-6 to omega-3 fatty acid ratio in sow diets alters serum, colostrum, and milk fatty acid profiles, but has minimal impact on reproductive performance. *Journal of Animal Science*, **92**, 5567-5582.

Farmer, C. and Petit, H.V. (2009) Effects of dietary supplementation with different forms of flax in late-gestation and lactation on fatty acid profiles in sows and their piglets. *Journal of Animal Science*, **87**, 2600-2613.

Farmer, C., Giguere, A. and Lessard, M. (2010) Dietary supplementation with different forms of flax in late gestation and lactation: Effects on sow and litter performances, endocrinology, and immune response. *Journal of Animal Science*, **88**, 225-237.

Food and Agricultural Organisation of the United Nations (2010) *Fats and fatty acids in human nutrition. Report of an expert consultation.* Food and Agricultural Organisation of the United Nations, Rome, Italy.

Gabler, N.K., Spencer, J.D., Webel, D.M. and Spurlock, M.E. (2007) In utero and postnatal exposure to long chain (n-3) PUFA enhances intestinal glucose absorption and energy stores in weanling pigs(1,2). *Journal of Nutrition*, **137**, 2351-2358.

Gabler, N.K., Radcliffe, J.S., Spencer, J.D., Webel, D.M. and Spurlock, M.E. (2009) Feeding long-chain n-3 polyunsaturated fatty acids during gestation increases intestinal glucose absorption potentially via the acute activation of AMPK. *Journal of Nutritional Biochemistry*, **20**, 17-25.

Laws, J., Litten, J.C., Laws, A., Lean, I.J., Dodds, P.F. and Clarke, L. (2009) Effect of type and timing of oil supplements to sows during pregnancy on the growth performance and endocrine profile of low and normal birth weight offspring. *British Journal of Nutrition*, **101**, 240-249.

Leonard, S.G., Sweeney, T., Bahar, B., Lynch, B.P. and O'Doherty, J.V. (2010) Effect of maternal fish oil and seaweed extract supplementation on colostrum and milk composition, humoral immune response, and performance of suckled piglets. *Journal of Animal Science*, **88**, 2988-2997.

Leskanich, C.O. and Noble, R.C. (1999) The comparative roles of polyunsaturated fatty acids in pig neonatal development. *British Journal of Nutrition*, **81**, 87-106.

Li, Z.Y., Kaplan, M.L. and Hachey, D.L. (2000) Hepatic microsomal and peroxisomal docosahexaenoate biosynthesis during piglet development. *Lipids*, **35**, 1325-1333.

Luo, J., Huang, F.R., Xiao, C.L., Chen, W., Jiang, S.W. and Peng, J. (2009) Effect of dietary supplementation of fish oil for lactating sows and weaned piglets on piglet Th polarization. *Livestock Science*, **126**, 286-291.

Millet, S. and Delezie, E. (2013) Should n-3 polyunsaturated fatty acids be included in the feed of reproducing animals? *Veterinary Journal*, **197**, 525-526.

National Research Council (2012) *Nutrient Requirements of Swine*. Eleventh Revised Edition edn. National Academic Press, Washington, USA

Nettleton J.A. (1995) *Omega-3 fatty acids and health*. Chapman and Hall, New York, USA.

Perez-Rigau, A., Lindemann, M., Kornegay, E., Harper A. and Watkins B. (1995) Role of dietary lipids on fetal tissue fatty acid composition and fetal survival in swine at 42 days of gestation. *Journal of Animal Science*, **73**, 1372-1380.

Pickard, R.M., Beard, A.R., Seal C.J. and Edwards, S.A. (2008) Neonatal lamb vigour is improved by feeding docosahexaenoic acid in the form of algal biomass during late gestation. *Animal*, **2**, 1186-1192.

Prates, E., Alves, S., Marques, C., Baptista, M., Horta, A., Bessa, R. and Pereira, R. (2013) Fatty acid composition of porcine cumulus oocyte complexes (COC) during maturation: effect of the lipid modulators trans-10, cis-12 conjugated linoleic acid (t10,c12 CLA) and forskolin. *In Vitro Cellular and Developmental Biology-Animal*, **49**, 335-345.

Rooke, J.A., Shanks M. and Edwards S.A. (2000) Effect of offering maize, linseed or tuna oils throughout pregnancy and lactation on sow and piglet tissue composition and piglet performance. *Animal Science*, **71**, 289-299.

Rooke, J.A., Sinclair, A.G. and Edwards, S.A. (2001a) Feeding tuna oil to the sow at different times during pregnancy has different effects on piglet long-chain polyunsaturated fatty acid composition at birth and subsequent growth. *British Journal of Nutrition*, **86**, 21-30.

Rooke, J.A., Sinclair, A.G. and Ewen, M. (2001b) Changes in piglet tissue composition at birth in response to increasing maternal intake of long-chain n-3 polyunsaturated fatty acids are non-linear. *British Journal of Nutrition*, **86**, 461-470.

Rooke, J.A., Ferguson, E.M., Sinclair, A.G. and Speake, B.K. (2003) Fatty acids and reproduction in the pig. In: *Recent Advances in Animal Nutrition 2003* (Eds. P.C. Garnsworthy and J. Wiseman) pp. 47-66. Nottingham University Press, Nottingham, UK

Sargeant, J.M., Rajic, A., Read, S. and Ohlsson, A. (2006) The process of systematic review and its application in agri-food public-health. *Preventive Veterinary Medicine*, **75**, 141-151.

Smit, M., Spencer, J., Patterson, J., Dyck, M., Dixon, W. and Foxcroft, G. (2015) Effects of dietary enrichment with a marine oil-based n-3 LCPUFA supplement in sows with predicted birth weight phenotypes on birth litter quality and growth performance to weaning. *Animal*, **9**, 471-480.

Smits, R., Luxford, B., Mitchell, M. and Nottle, M. (2011) Sow litter size is increased in the subsequent parity when lactating sows are fed diets containing n-3 fatty acids from fish oil. *Journal of Animal Science*, **89**, 2731-2738.

Smits, R., Luxford, B., Mitchell, M. and Nottle, M. (2013) Embryo survival, but not first-parity litter size, is increased when gilts are fed diets supplemented with omega-3 fatty acids from fish oil. *Animal Production Science*, **53**, 57-66.

Speake, B.K., Surai, P.F. and Rooke, J.A. (20030 Regulation of avian and mammalian sperm production by dietary fatty acids. In: S.R. De Vriese and; A.B. Christophe (eds.), *Male Fertility and Lipid Metabolism*. AOCS Press, Champaign IL, USA, 96-117.

Sprecher, H. (2000) Metabolism of highly unsaturated n-3 and n-6 fatty acids. Biochimica et *Biophysica Acta-Molecular and Cell Biology of Lipids*, **1486**, 219-231.

Strzezek, J., Fraser, L. and Kuklinska, M., Dziekonska, A. and Lecewicz, M. (2004) Effects of dietary supplementation with polyunsaturated fatty acids and antioxidants on biochemical characteristics of boar semen. *Reproductive Biology*, **4**, 271-287.

Sturmey, R.G., Reis, A., Leese, H.J. and McEvoy, T.G. (2009) Role of fatty acids in energy provision during oocyte maturation and early embryo development. *Reproduction in Domestic Animals*, **44**, 50-58.

Tanghe, S. and De Smet, S. (2013) Does sow reproduction and piglet performance benefit from the addition of n-3 polyunsaturated fatty acids to the maternal diet? *Veterinary Journal*, **197**, 560-569.

Tanghe, S., Millet, S. and De Smet, S. (2013) Echium oil and linseed oil as alternatives for fish oil in the maternal diet: Blood fatty acid profiles and oxidative status of sows and piglets. *Journal of Animal Science*, **91**, 3253-3264.

Tanghe, S., Missotten, J., Raes, K., Vangeyte, J. and De Smet, S. (2014a) Diverse effects of linseed oil and fish oil in diets for sows on reproductive performance and pre-weaning growth of piglets. *Livestock Science*, **164**, 109-118.

Tanghe, S., Millet, S., Missotten, J., Vlaeminck, B. and De Smet, S. (2014b) Effects of birth weight and maternal dietary fat source on the fatty acid profile of piglet tissue. *Animal*, **8**, 1857-1866.

Tanghe, S., Cox, E., Melkebeek, V., De Smet, S. and Millet, S. (2014c) Effect of fatty acid composition of the sow diet on the innate and adaptive immunity of the piglets after weaning. *Veterinary Journal*, **200**, 287-293.

Tocher, D.R. (2009) Issues surrounding fish as a source of omega-3 long-chain polyunsaturated fatty acids. *Lipid Technology*, **21**, 13-16.

Vallet, J., Rempel, L., Miles, J. and Webel, S. (2014) Effect of essential fatty acid and zinc supplementation during pregnancy on birth intervals, neonatal piglet brain myelination, stillbirth, and preweaning mortality. *Journal of Animal Science*, **92**, 2422-2432.

Yeste, M., Barrera, X., Coll, D. and Bonet, S. (2011) The effects on boar sperm quality of dietary supplementation with omega-3 polyunsaturated fatty acids differ among porcine breeds. *Theriogenology*, **76**, 184-196.

11

Transgenic Camelina Sativa As A Source Of Oils To Replace Marine Fish Oil In Aquaculture Feeds

J.A. NAPIER[1], M.B. BETANCOR[2], M. SPRAGUE[2], O. SAYANOVA[1], S. USHER[1], P.J. CAMPBELL[3], D.R. TOCHER[2]

[1] *Department of Biological Chemistry and Crop Protection, Rothamsted Research, Harpenden AL5 2JQ, United Kingdom*

[2] *Institute of Aquaculture, School of Natural Sciences, Stirling University, Stirling, FK9 4LA, United Kingdom*

[3] *Biomar Ltd., North Shore Road, Grangemouth FK3 8UL, United Kingdom*

Introduction

Marine fish oils are a finite and limited resource and the use of high levels in aquafeeds is a non-sustainable practice (Tocher, 2015). Alternative oils sourced from terrestrial plants do not contain omega-3 long-chain polyunsaturated fatty acids (LC-PUFA), therefore, feeds based on conventional vegetable oils reduce levels of eicosapentaenoic acid (EPA) and docosahexaenoic acid (DHA) in farmed fish (Turchini *et al.*, 2010). Consequently, the aquaculture industry requires new oil sources that contain high levels of omega-3 LC-PUFA to supply the increasing demand for fish and seafood while maintaining the high nutritional quality of farmed products. One viable approach to the renewable supply of omega-3 LC-PUFA is metabolic engineering oilseed crops with the capacity to synthesize these critical fatty acids (Sayanova and Napier, 2011). Recently, the oilseed Camelina sativa has been transformed with algal genes encoding the omega-3 biosynthetic pathway and expression restricted to the seeds via seed-specific promoters to produce oils containing either EPA alone or EPA and DHA (Ruiz-Lopez *et al.*, 2014). These oils were investigated as replacements for marine fish oil in feeds for Atlantic salmon (Salmo salar) and gilthead sea bream (Sparus aurata). In addition to assessing the ability of these novel oils to maintain the nutritional quality of farmed fish, these studies have contributed to our understanding of the biochemical and molecular mechanisms involved in the control and regulation of DHA production from EPA, and thus better inform our understanding of the LC-PUFA biosynthetic pathway in salmonids and marine fish species. Moreover, such studies demonstrate the feasibility of using this novel GM oil as a safe, sustainable and economically viable replacement for oceanic sources of these important fatty acids.

Materials and methods

Isonitrogenous and isoenergetic diets were formulated to satisfy the nutritional requirements of salmon and sea bream (NRC, 2011). The diets for salmon supplied 45-46 g/kg crude protein and 21-25 g/kg crude lipid (depending upon trial), and the sea bream diets supplied 50 g/kg crude protein and 17 g/kg crude lipid and were manufactured at BioMar Tech-Centre (Brande, Denmark). For each species, the diets had the same basal composition with added oil supplied by fish oil (FO), wild-type Camelina oil (WCO) or EPA-Camelina oil (ECO) or EPA/DHA-Camelina oil (DCO). The fatty acid compositions of the feeds are shown in Table 1. Non-defatted fishmeal was employed as the major protein source to ensure EFA requirements were met. Ytrium oxide was added to the experimental diets (0.5 g/kg) as an inert marker for calculation of lipid and fatty acid digestibility. For the Atlantic salmon trials, post-smolts were distributed into seawater tanks (45 fish per tank) and fed the three experimental feeds in triplicate for 7-8 weeks. The experimental system comprised 1 m2, 500 L tanks supplied by flow-through seawater (15 L/min) at ambient temperature that averaged 10.2 ± 0.6 °C. Similarly, sea bream of initial size 50 g were distributed into 12 x 1000 L tanks (35 fish per tank) supplied by flow-through filtered seawater at an ambient temperature of 19.5 °C and fed the four experimental feeds in triplicate for 12 weeks. Prior to the initiation of the feeding trials, all fish were acclimated for 1 week during which time they were fed the WCO diet. For salmon, feeds were delivered in excess by automatic disc feeders with an automated uneaten feed collection system. For sea bream, feeds were delivered by hand to satiety twice daily. Growth performance, feed efficiency and fish health were determined along with nutrient and fatty acid composition. In addition, the metabolic/molecular consequences of this new ingredient were assessed by analysis of gene expression using oligonucleotide microarray and/or quantitative RT-PCR.

Results and discussion

There is a global lack of the omega-3 LC-PUFA, EPA and DHA, to satisfy current human dietary requirements (Tocher, 2015). As fish and seafood are the main sources of these critical nutrients in the human diet, and as the majority is now farmed, there is pressure on aquaculture to maintain the health-promoting benefits of the farmed products. Entirely new sources of omega-3 LC-PUFA are required and, currently, oils from transgenic oilseed crops represent the only feasible option that can supply the

Table 1. Fatty acid compositions (%) of experimental feeds fed to Atlantic salmon and sea bream

	Salmon 1			Salmon 2			Sea bream			
	FO	WCO	ECO	FO	WCO	DCO	FO	WCO	ECO	DCO
Σ Saturated	30.7	13.4	17.4	31.3	12.8	17.4	29.7	14.8	17.5	18.4
Σ monoenes	26.6	37.0	18.2	27.8	33.2	21.4	27.8	32.9	21.6	22.7
18:2n-6	3.6	17.5	19.1	2.7	17.5	19.1	5.6	18.0	21.4	19.3
20:4n-6	0.9	0.1	2.5	1.3	0.1	1.8	1.2	0.2	2.6	1.6
Σ n-6 PUFA	5.3	19.0	25.7	4.9	19.6	27.2	7.8	19.7	27.9	26.3
18:3n-3	1.0	25.4	10.5	0.8	27.6	12.4	1.0	23.3	8.4	10.7
18:4n-3	2.5	0.5	1.4	2.1	0.4	3.8	2.0	0.6	1.1	3.4
20:3n-3	0.1	1.3	1.0	0.1	1.1	0.6	0.1	1.0	0.8	0.6
20:4n-3	0.7	0.0	3.0	0.6	0.1	2.0	0.6	0.1	2.3	1.8
20:5n-3	16.0	0.1	18.8	15.4	1.7	6.5	14.2	2.4	14.2	6.6
22:5n-3	1.8	0.3	1.0	1.8	0.2	1.5	1.6	0.3	0.9	1.4
22:6n-3	11.2	2.5	2.4	10.8	3.0	7.0	11.3	4.5	4.8	7.9
Σ n-3 PUFA	33.2	30.0	38.0	31.5	34.1	33.7	30.7	32.2	32.5	32.2
Σ n-3 LC-PUFA	29.7	2.9	25.2	28.6	5.0	17.0	27.7	7.3	22.2	17.7

Σ n-3 LC-PUFA (≥ C20 and ≥ 4 double bonds, i.e. 20:4+20:5+22:5+22:6

volumes of EPA- and DHA-rich oil at a likely cost that animal production can afford. The results of the present studies will demonstrate that oils derived from transgenic oilseed crops are effective, safe replacements for marine fish oils in aquaculture feeds that can maintain high levels of omega-3 LC-PUFA.

Acknowledgments

Rothamsted Research receives grant-aided support from the Biotechnology and Biological Sciences Research Council (BBSRC). This project was partly funded by a BBSRC UK Industrial Partnership Award (BB/J00166X/1 and BB/J001252/1). The sea bream trial was partly supported by a Trans-National Access grant (0119/08/12/28) from the EU FP7 CP-CSA Project 262336 Aquaculture infrastructures for excellence in European fish research (AQUAEXCEL), and a Santander University Staff Mobility Fund award to MBB.

References

National Research Council (NRC), 2011. *Nutrient requirements of fish and shrimp*. The National Academies Press, Washington D.C.

Ruiz-Lopez, N., R.P. Haslam, J.A. Napier, O. Sayanova. 2014. Successful high-level accumulation of fish oil omega-3 long-chain polyunsaturated fatty acids in a transgenic oilseed crop. *The Plant Journal*, **77**, 198-208.

Sayanova, O., J.A. Napier. 2011. Transgenic oilseed crops as an alternative to fish oils. *Prostaglandins, Leukotrienes and Essential Fatty Acids*, **85**, 253-260.

Tocher, D.R. 2015. Omega-3 long-chain polyunsaturated fatty acids and aquaculture in perspective. *Aquaculture, in press* (doi.org/10.1016/j.aquaculture.2015.01.010).

Turchini, G.M., W.-K. Ng, D.R. Tocher. (Eds.) 2010. *Fish Oil Replacement and Alternative Lipid Sources in Aquaculture Feeds*. Taylor & Francis, CRC Press, Boca Raton. 533p.

12

Fermented Products And Diets For Pigs

C.L. WALK

AB Vista, Marlborough UK

Summary

Dietary calcium (Ca) is often over-fed in pig diets due to high variability in the Ca concentration in feed ingredients. When comparing book values or descriptive terms for dietary Ca, it is generally only discussed as total Ca rather than digestible Ca or available Ca. Supplying Ca in the diet is relatively cheap, but feeding higher than formulated dietary Ca can have negative effects on the digestibility of more expensive ingredients such as crude protein, amino acids and phosphorus (P). Therefore, establishing a digestible Ca requirement in pigs may provide a more representative ingredient and diet Ca concentrations and mitigate some of the negative impacts of high dietary Ca on animal performance and nutrient digestibility. A series of experiments have been conducted to design a method to evaluate the digestible Ca concentration of various inorganic and organic feed ingredients, and to use these values to establish a digestible Ca requirement for pigs based on growth performance, Ca and P balance and bone ash.

Total calcium

When discussing nutrient costs and inclusion levels in non-ruminant diets, Ca is considered one of the cheapest and quite possibly the most easily supplied nutrient. Calcium carbonate is rich in Ca (380g/kg) and inorganic phosphate sources such as mono- or dicalcium phosphate also supply around 160-250g Ca/kg. Calcium is also found at 40-100g Ca/kg in meat and bone meal and fish meal and at up to 120g Ca/kg when added as a carrier in vitamin and mineral premixes (Table 1). In addition, some grains, such as canola meal, soyabean meal, cottonseed meal and sunflower meal, contain Ca between 2.5 and 6.9g Ca/kg (Gonzalez-Vega and Stein, 2014), which could represent up to 14% of total Ca supplied in the diet (Table 1). Concentrations of Ca in ingredients may also vary depending on nutrient specification guidelines employed. For example, when the same piglet diet was formulated using Ca specifications from three different nutrient guidelines, the calculated difference in Ca concentration in the diet could be as high as 42.9% (Table 1). No single value is absolutely correct and more likely Ca should be analysed in feed ingredients prior to feed formulation to build a database of Ca values, bearing in mind the usual high variation associated with the Ca assay and contamination from water, glassware and other sources.

Table 1. Concentration (g/kg) of calcium in various feed ingredients and contribution of calcium from these ingredients in a complete diet

Calcium source	Ca[A],	Ca[B],	Ca[C],	Example diet[D],	Ca diet[A], g/kg	Ca diet[B],	Difference [A] vs [B], %	Ca diet[C],	Difference [A] vs [C], %
Inorganic sources									
Calcium carbonate	385.0			4.5	1.7				
Dicalcium phosphate	248.0	245.0							
Limestone	358.0	380.0							
Monocalcium phosphate	169.0	175.0		10.8	1.8	1.9	5.3		
Grains									
Canola meal	6.9	8.0	6.3						
Corn	0.2	0.3	0.3	238.5	0.04	0.07	42.9	0.07	42.9
Corn germ meal	1.8	0.5	0.2						
Cottonseed meal	2.5	1.9							
Soybean meal	3.3	3.2	3.2	202.3	0.7	0.6	14.3	0.6	14.3
Sunflower meal	3.9	3.5	3.7						
Wheat	0.6	0.4	0.6						
Organic sources									
Fish meal	42.8	23.8	52.1	50.0	2.1	1.2	42.9	2.6	19.2
Meat and bone meal	109.0	102.0	98.7						
Poultry by product meal	45.4	51.0							
Whey	6.2	8.0	7.5	50.0	0.3	0.4	25.0	0.4	25.0
Vitamin and mineral premix		123.8		5.0		0.6			

[A] Total calcium values were obtained from the Swine NRC, 2012 and modified from Gonzalez-Vega and Stein, 2014.
[B] Total calcium values were obtained from the Premier Nutrition Atlas, 2014 (AB Agri Limited, Rugeley UK), with the exception of the vitamin and mineral premix which was obtained from an example premix (Premier Nutrition Products, Rugeley UK).
[C] National Swine Nutrition Guide version 1.2.
[D] Nutrient adequate pig diet obtained from Walk et al., 2013.

Due to being a low cost nutrient, abundant in feed ingredients and contamination from other sources or through addition of limestone to add bulk to diets, Ca is commonly over-supplied in non-ruminant diets. For example, when total Ca was analysed in 357 pig diets, 2.4g total Ca/kg was unaccounted for in the diet (Figure 1). This means if a diet was formulated to contain 8g/kg total Ca, the analysed value could be as high as 10.4g Ca/kg or almost 25% above the expected dietary Ca concentration. When total P was analysed in 359 pig diets, 1.2g total P/kg was unaccounted for in the feed formulation (Figure 2). The difference between expected and analysed total P and expected and analysed total Ca in the diet may be associated with the higher cost of P and the numerous descriptors for dietary P, such as phytate P, non-phytate P, available P, total P or digestible P, but only total Ca is used to represent dietary Ca.

The discrepancy between expected and analysed total Ca may have implications on more expensive nutrients. For example, high dietary Ca has been reported to reduce average daily gain (ADG), feed efficiency and P digestibility in pigs (Gonzalez-Vega *et al.*, 2015a) and P and crude protein digestibility in broilers due to an increase in gastrointestinal pH (Walk *et al.*, 2012). One way to account better for dietary Ca in feed ingredients may be to establish a digestible Ca concentration and a subsequent digestible Ca requirement for pigs, similar to a digestible P or digestible amino acid requirement. This chapter focuses on the research and methods used to establish standardised total tract digestible (STTD) Ca values for various feed ingredients, and eventually determine the digestible Ca requirement of pigs.

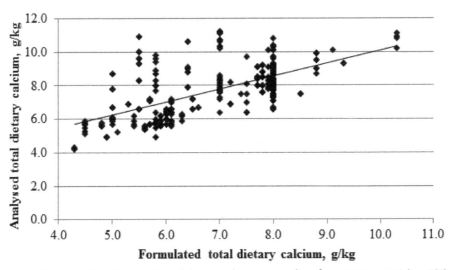

Figure 1. Formulated and analysed total dietary calcium in pig diets from 2010 to 2015 (n = 357). R2 = 0.37; y = 0.7728x + 2.3685. RMSE = 1.217.

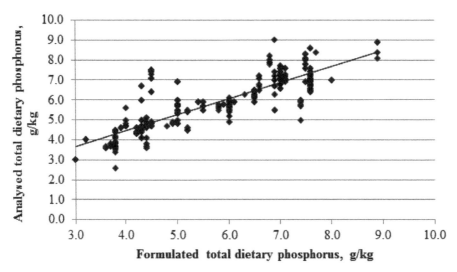

Figure 2. Formulated and analysed total dietary phosphorus in pig diets from 2010 to 2015 (n = 359). R2 = 0.72; y = 0.8017x + 1.2607. RMSE = 0.734.

Establishing a method to evaluate digestible calcium concentration in ingredients

Prior to determining apparent total tract digestibility (ATTD) or STTD of Ca in various feed ingredients, it was important to set method and experimental parameters to use in subsequent trials. Therefore, a series of experiments were designed to determine if measurable amounts of endogenous Ca were lost in the gastrointestinal tract, and if so, if ATTD and true total tract digestibility (TTTD) of Ca differed sufficiently to warrant a TTTD system, and finally to evaluate influence of the basal diet on STTD of Ca. Estimated total endogenous loss of Ca was approximately 0.11 to 0.13 g Ca per day (Gonzalez-Vega *et al.*, 2013) and this could arise from saliva, pancreatic secretions, epithelial cells, bile, intestinal enzymes or mucin. When ATTD of Ca was corrected for basal endogenous losses (TTTD), there were differences between ATTD and TTTD, and ATTD increased with Ca intake whereas TTTD did not (Gonzalez-Vega *et al.*, 2013). Therefore, TTTD of Ca is not influenced by Ca concentration in the diet or ingredient, and would be additive in mixed diets, similar to amino acids and P.

The previous trial evaluated endogenous losses of Ca using canola meal as the only source of Ca and kept digestible P concentration in the diet at requirement levels (3.2g digestible P/kg) according to the Swine NRC (2012). Canola meal has a relatively high concentration of Ca (6.6g/kg) and a subsequent trial used fish meal as the sole source of Ca (Gonzalez-Vega *et al.*, 2015c); this trial revealed that the diet employed in the evaluation of STTD of fish meal Ca has a significant effect on STTD of Ca.

For example, when the test diet contained predominantly maize-starch (synthetic diet), the content of STTD Ca in fish meal was 456.4g/kg. However, if fibre (Solka Floc; Fibre Sales and Development Corp, Urbana, OH) was added to the synthetic diet, the content of STTD Ca in fish meal was increased significantly (P < 0.001) to 622.3g/kg. If the diet contained predominantly maize, which is low in Ca, content of STTD Ca in fish meal increased (P < 0.001) even further, to 889.9g/kg. Therefore, determined STTD of Ca in various feed ingredients will be significantly different depending on use of synthetic or semi-synthetic diets. To ensure accurate reflections of STTD Ca values for feed ingredients, test diets should be similar to commercial diets, containing maize or wheat, which is low in Ca, and allowing for a high contribution of dietary Ca to come from the ingredient being evaluated.

The digestible calcium concentration of various feed ingredients

Using previously-determined basal endogenous losses of Ca and maize as the predominant ingredient, Gonzalez-Vega et al. (2015a,b) conducted a series of experiments to evaluate differences in STTD of Ca between inorganic Ca sources and to determine STTD of Ca values for inorganic ingredients. In the process, STTD of Ca in canola, fish meal and maize was also obtained (Table 2). The authors reported STTD of Ca was higher (P < 0.001) in monocalcium phosphate and dicalcium phosphate compared with STTD of Ca in Ca carbonate. Piglets fed salmon bones (Malde et al., 2010) or Ca citrate (Jiang et al., 2013) had higher Ca digestibility than piglets fed Ca carbonate. However, evaluation of STTD Ca in ingredients fed to pigs is limited. Subsequent trials to evaluate organic sources or novel sources of Ca are in process to understand better Ca requirements and digestibility in pigs.

Table 2. Coefficient of standardised total tract digestibility (STTD) of Ca in ingredients (modified from Gonzalez-Vega et al., 2015a,b,c)

Calcium source	Analysed Ca, g/kg	STTD Ca
Inorganic sources		
Calcium carbonate	418.2	0.604
Dicalcium phosphate	216.1	0.778
Monocalcium phosphate	185.4	0.859
Organic sources		
Canola meal	6.6	0.466[1]
Maize	0.1	0.689
Fish meal	56.9	0.890

[1] True total tract digestible Ca.

Other factors that can influence digestible calcium requirement

Phytase

Inclusion of phytase into growing pig diets increased digestibility of Ca and also P through hydrolysis of phytate (Kuehn and Manner, 2012). However, the magnitude of the response and therefore the influence of phytase on Ca digestibility may be dependent on source of Ca in the diet and its binding affinity to phytate. For example, Gonzalez-Vega et al. (2015a) reported phytase supplementation had no effect on STTD of Ca in inorganic Ca sources, but increased (P < 0.001) STTD of Ca in the complete diets, regardless of the Ca source (Table 3); the authors reported a tendency (P = 0.106) towards a higher response to phytase in the diets containing no supplemental Ca or Ca carbonate compared with the diets containing mono- or dicalcium phosphate. Phytase improved STTD of Ca in the non-supplemented diet by 13.9% and the Ca carbonate diet by 10.1%, compared to 4.2 in the mono-calcium phosphate diet and 2.8% in the dicalcium phosphate diets. The lack of effect of phytase on STTD of Ca in the Ca ingredients was expected due to the absence of phytate. However the results indicate there was a relationship between Ca and phytate in the diets, and the magnitude of the response to phytase may be associated with Ca source, binding affinity of Ca to phytate and Ca to P ratio, which changed with addition of phosphate from mono- and dicalcium phosphate. Additionally, phytase increased (P < 0.01) STTD of Ca in fish meal (Table 3), indicating phytase increases digestibility of Ca in organic as well as inorganic sources (Gonzalez-Vega et al., 2015b). The previous results also indicate that Ca from fishmeal can bind to phytate in the gastrointestinal tract and become less available for absorption. The

Table 3. Standardised total tract digestibility (STTD) of Ca in ingredients (modified from Gonzalez-Vega et al., 2015a,b,c)

Calcium source	Analysed Ca, g/kg	Coefficient of STTD Ca No phytase	Phytase
Inorganic sources			
Calcium carbonate[1]	418.2	0.640	0.712
Dicalcium phosphate[1]	216.1	0.727	0.748
Monocalcium phosphate[1]	185.4	0.767	0.800
Organic sources			
Canola meal[2]	6.6	0.466[4]	0.703[4]
Maize[1]	0.1	0.689	0.800
Fish meal[3]	56.9	0.762	0.869

[1] Ca source P < 0.001, Phytase P < 0.001, Ca source × phytase P = 0.11.
[2] Ca level P = 0.86, Phytase P < 0.01, Ca level × phytase P = 0.55.
[3] Diet P < 0.001, Phytase P = 0.009, Diet × phytase P = 0.46.
[4] True total tract digestible Ca.

ability of phytase to improve Ca digestibility has been reported previously (Kuhn and Manner, 2012; Gonzalez-Vega *et al.*, 2013). When using STTD Ca values rather than total Ca values in diets, the Ca matrix applied with a phytase could be the same as when applying a digestible P matrix, as the amount of Ca removed from the diet is based on the digestible Ca value, rather than a total Ca value.

Calcium to phosphorus ratio

Digestible P concentration in the diets of the previously mentioned trials was maintained at Swine NRC (2012) requirements and therefore the only factors measured were influence of Ca source, diet type, phytate or Ca level on STTD of Ca. However, as Ca concentration in the diet increased, Ca to P ratio would change depending on source of Ca, and this effect cannot be ignored in the current set of data. This is especially true in diets formulated with mono- or dicalcium phosphate since source of phosphate in the diet changed from phytate P to inorganic P with supplementation of mono- or dicalcium phosphate. Fan and Archbold (2012) reported optimal response in feed efficiency and P digestibility was obtained in growing pigs fed diets with a true faecal digestible Ca to P ratio around 1.0:1.0. These results are similar to those of Liu *et al.* (2000), who reported pigs fed a Ca to total P ratio at 1.0:1.0 in low P diets containing phytase had increased apparent absorption of P in the small intestine. When dietary Ca concentration was increased with inclusion of canola meal, Ca to total P ratio in the diet increased from 0.29:1 to 0.48:1 and thus the Ca to P ratio was well below optimum (Gonzalez-Vega *et al.*, 2013). However, when mono- or dicalcium phosphate was supplied in the diets as an inorganic Ca source, the Ca to total P ratio was 1.09:1 or 1.18:1, respectively (Gonzalez-Vega *et al.*, 2015b) and thus closer to the optimum Ca to P ratios reported by Fan and Archbold (2012) and Liu *et al.* (2000), and may have resulted in the higher STTD of Ca in those ingredients. The Ca to P ratio influences Ca and P balance and is an important regulator of Ca or P excretion in urine. Calcium may be absorbed in the small intestine, but in the absence of enough P, as found in diets with a high Ca to P ratio, Ca may be excreted in the urine rather than absorbed and utilised by the animal (Gonzalez-Vega *et al.*, 2013).

Conclusions

Dietary Ca is often over-fed in pig diets with an average of 2.4g total Ca/kg unaccounted for in the diet. Published dietary Ca concentrations in feed ingredients are highly variable and this variation could result in large differences in the expected dietary contribution of Ca from those same ingredients. Establishing a digestible Ca concentration for commonly used feed ingredients and a subsequent digestible

Ca requirement may facilitate better understanding of Ca concentration in feed ingredients and also Ca requirements of animals.

The results from the series of experiments conducted by Gonzalez-Vega *et al.*, (2013, 2014, 2015a,b,c) indicate there are measurable losses of endogenous Ca in the gastrointestinal tract. Therefore, TTTD or STTD of Ca in ingredients should be additive in mixed diets and not influenced by dietary concentration of Ca. Phytase significantly improved STTD of Ca in diets, but had no influence on STTD of Ca in ingredients. Finally, the predominant use of purified starch in the low- or Ca-free test diet may have an influence on STTD of Ca. Therefore, the use of maize or wheat as the low Ca source of energy should be considered since this resembles diets and ingredients used in commercial conditions. With the previously determined STTD Ca concentrations for Ca carbonate, mono- or dicalcium phosphate, maize, canola meal and fish meal, we are able to evaluate STTD Ca requirement in pigs using growth performance, bone ash and Ca and P balance as parameters at various feeding phases. These results will provide a better understanding of Ca requirement for pigs, variation of Ca in feed ingredients, and a more precise set of nutrient formulations, similar to what is currently done with digestible P and digestible amino acids. Formulating pig diets to more precise nutrient requirements will result in improved P, crude protein and amino acid and Ca digestibility and subsequently have a positive influence on growth performance, skeletal integrity and feed efficiency.

References

Fan, M.Z. and Archbold, T. (2012) Effects of dietary true digestible calcium to phosphorus ratio on growth performance and efficiency of calcium and phosphorus use in growing pigs fed corn and soybean meal-based diets. *Journal of Animal Science*, **90**, 254-256.

Gonzalez-Vega, J.C., Walk, C.L. and Stein, H.H. (2013) Determination of endogenous intestinal losses of calcium and true total tract digestibility of calcium in canola meal fed to growing pigs. *Journal of Animal Science*, **91**, 4807-4816.

Gonzalez-Vega, J.C. and Stein, H.H. (2014) Calcium digestibility and metabolism in pigs. Asian Australian. *Journal of Animal Science*, **27**, 1-9.

Gonzalez-Vega, J.C., Walk, C.L. and Stein, H.H. (2015a) Digestible calcium requirements and calcium and phosphorus balance for weanling pigs. *Journal of Animal Science* (in press).

Gonzalez-Vega, J.C., Walk, C.L. and Stein, H.H. (2015b) Effects of microbial phytase on apparent and standardized total tract digestibility of calcium in calcium supplements fed to growing pigs. *Journal of Animal Science* (in press).

Gonzalez-Vega, J.C., Walk, C.L. and Stein, H.H. (2015c) Effect of microbial phytase, fiber and soybean oil on calculated values for apparent and standardized total tract digestibility of calcium in fish meal. *Journal of Animal Science* (in press).

Jiang, H., Wang, J., Che, L., Lin, Y., Fang, Z. and Wu, D. (2013) Effects of calcium sources and levels on growth performance and calcium bioavailability in weaning piglets. *Asian Journal of Animal and Veterinary Advances,* **8**, 613-621.

Kuhn, I. and Manner, K. (2012) Performance and apparent total tract phosphorus and calcium digestibility in grower-finisher pigs fed diets with and without phytase. *Journal of Animal Science*, **90**, 143-145.

Liu, J., Bollinger, D.W., Ledoux, D.R. and Venum, T.L. (2000) Effects of dietary calcium: phosphorus ratios on apparent absorption of calcium and phosphorus in the small intestine, cecum and colon of pigs. *Journal of Animal Science*, **78**, 106-109.

Malde, M.K., Graff, I.E., Siljander-Rasi, H., Venalainen, E., Julshamn, K., Pedersen, J.I. and Valaja, J. (2010) Fish bones – a highly available calcium source for growing pigs. *Journal of Animal Physiology and Animal Nutrition*, **94**, 66-76.

National Research Council (2012) Nutrient requirements of swine. 11th ed. National Academy Press, Washington, DC.

Walk, C.L., Srinongkote, S. and Wilcock, P. (2013) Influence of a microbial phytase and zinc oxide on young pig growth performance and serum minerals. *Journal of Animal Science*, **91**, 286-291.

Walk, C.L., Bedford, M.R. and McElroy, A.P. (2012) Influence of limestone and phytase on broiler performance, gastrointestinal pH, and apparent ileal nutrient digestibility. *Poultry Science*, **91**, 1371-1378.

13

The Pig: 2025

G.A. WALLING

JSR Genetics Limited, Southburn, Driffield, East Yorkshire, YO25 9ED, UK

Introduction

The pig has changed significantly during its evolution from Wild Boar to domesticated farm livestock species. However the more remarkable change has been the differences achieved over the last 40 years in the levels of efficiency and productivity. Annual output of the sow has more than doubled whilst growth and efficiency has improved 50-100% from the norms of the 1970s and 1980s. This changed has been delivered almost exclusively by genetics where changes are cumulative, permanent and sustainable in contrast to many other technologies that are neither repeatable nor sustainable for pig production businesses.

Changes elsewhere in the industry have not necessarily kept up with the rates of genetic change. Welfare codes are often "set in stone" and hence fail to meet the requirements of the modern animal and other allied support industries to pig production occasionally rely on the "tried and tested" rather than the levels of innovation required to meet the demands of the modern pig.

The rate of progress in genetic improvement in pig production will not slow. Indeed with modern techniques and methods the selection process is now more accurate and efficient than ever, meaning progress is likely to be quicker. The traits of emphasis however are changing, mainly due to the previous success of selection. Increased litter size has no value if the sow is unable to rear the piglets or if the birth weight decreases below a point that is viable on farm. Hence the coming decade is likely to change the domestic pig into an animal better suited to modern farming rather than boosting productivity and efficiency statistics alone. Robustness is hence a key breeding company buzzword despite being difficult to quantify.

The future sow

The current sow is hugely successful, enabling many farms globally to achieve in excess of 30 pigs weaned per sow per year but this success is also causing the greatest challenges. Many of the changes to the sow in the next decade are required because of problems arising through the success of selection for litter size during the last 20 years. Sow longevity and piglet birth weight has decreased, age at first insemination has increased and numbers weaned per litter or number of teats on the sow has not kept pace with the large increases in numbers born alive. Further, the sow has become a more challenging animal to farm with feed intake in the farrowing house often a concern during warmer months.

The sow in 2025 should be capable of producing and rearing 6 good litters of pigs during her productive lifetime on the farm (in excess of 13.5 weaned per litter). To achieve this the sow is likely to need to produce an average litter size of 14.5 piglets up to 1.6kg average birthweight with a maximum spread of 300g from the smallest to largest animal. To feed this litter the sow will need a minimum of 15 functional teats. Systems and farms vary around the world and the figures quoted are based on relatively modern farms however a sow should be "fit for purpose" for the farm whether it be indoor or outdoor, modern high health or older with endemic diseases. The best indicator of this is the necessary replacement rate of sows which should be targeted at 50%. The future sow should also have high levels of resilience (not resistance per se) to typical endemic disease such as PRRS through a high level of generalised immunity.

The future slaughter pig

The time has come to stop concentrating on individual statistics at a specific point in an animal's lifetime and concentrate on a more holistic approach. The purpose of pig production is the production of slaughter pigs and ultimately pigmeat, not maximising profitability through an individual phase of growth and development. Focus on pre-weaning mortality or finisher growth rate will therefore become irrelevant if the equivalent figures at other phases are not economically sustainable. The focus on individual phases is useful as a management tool but the pig industry will have to be better communicators of standards and performance in the coming decade with increased focus from the consumer on where and how food is produced.

The slaughter pig in 2025 will be weaned in excess of 8kg and will should be aiming for a lifetime mortality figure i.e. proportion of animals that fail to be sold as slaughter pigs , of less than 10%. Predicting future slaughter weights is very dependent on individual market requirement but assuming castration is globally unacceptable by 2025 an estimated target slaughter weight of 127kg liveweight at 22 weeks of age would be indicative of a weaning to finish growth rate of ~915g/day. With demand for cereals likely to rise with an increasing global population alternative food sources will have to become more mainstream and with costs of food sources only likely to increase, lifetime FCR must stay below 2.0. Whilst endemic disease is still likely to challenge the industry this will have to be met through genetic resilience and generalised immunity as antibiotics are likely to be reserved for the most deserving human cases and not a tool to be (ab)used by the livestock industry.

The future carcase

Based on UK slaughter specifications the 127kg liveweight animal is likely to provide a 90-95kg carcass. Penalties for fatness levels in this carcase will become irrelevant as pressure on pig production for low FCR and production efficiency will ensure carcases do not become excessively fat. Instead the key performance indicators will move towards traits valued by the processor and ultimately the consumer. For the processor a better system of rewarding saleable meat such as using primal yield and pH (as an indicator of drip loss and hence percentage sold). Consumers however are more likely to focus on either meat eating quality or nutritional traits. It is for that reason that minimum intramuscular fat levels of 3.5% or slice shear force values below 12kg would be required for higher meat eating quality product. Healthier products in contrast may choose to use fat percentage taken whilst primal yield is measured but even the constitution of the fat may be measured using techniques such as the fat iodine value with an upper limit threshold of 65 used to distinguish healthier product.

14

Trends And Opportunities In The UK Pig Feed Market And Supply Trade

S. HOWARTH

Market Specialist Manager, AHDB Pork, Stoneleigh Park, Kenilworth, Warwickshire CV8 2TL.

The UK pig industry

UK pig herd trends

Latest figures from Defra show that in December 2014, the UK pig herd was above 4.5 million head for the first time since 2008, up nearly 130,000 (3%) over the preceding year (Table 1). This shows that productivity is improving, given that the number of sows was down by 8,000 head (2%). The overall increase was, therefore, due to a 140,000 head (4%) rise in the number of feeding pigs.

Table 1. Pigs on agricultural holdings in the UK, December, 2012 – 2014

Thousand Head	2012	2013	2014
Total pigs	4,216	4,383	4,510
Breeding Pigs	509	497	486
Female breeding herd	400	398	390
Sows in pig	269	273	260
Gilts in pig	68	60	56
Other sows (suckling or dry)	63	64	74
Other breeding pigs	109	99	96
Boars for service	15	15	13
Maiden gilts	93	84	83
Feeding pigs (incl. barren sows)	3,707	3,886	4,024

Source: Defra December Survey of Pigs

The recent increase in pig numbers marks a reversal of the trend which has seen the UK pig herd decline by nearly half since the late 1990s. Most of the decline occurred between 1998 and 2003, with numbers having only declined modestly since then. This decline was caused by a combination of factors which occurred together to impact severely on the competitiveness of the UK pig industry.

Until the mid-1990s, the UK pig herd had been broadly stable but followed a cyclical pattern typical of many agricultural sectors. The herd size peaked roughly every five years at which point reduced prices due to excess supply led to a contraction, pushing prices higher in due course.

In the mid-1990s, increased demand for pork following publicity about BSE in beef led to a surge in prices across the EU. With producers making good profits, many chose to expand. This led to an over-supply of pigs across the EU and prices fell sharply. In 1996, the average GB pig price was a then record 136.51p per carcase kg; by 1998, it had fallen to 80.75p/kg, the lowest for many years.

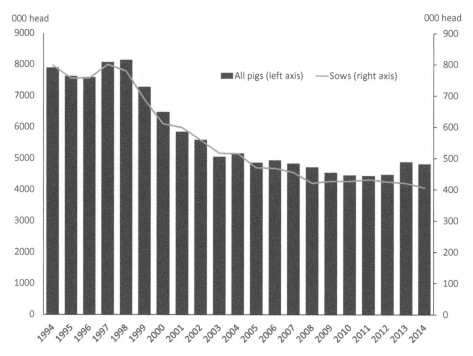

Source: Defra June Agricultural Survey
Figure 1. UK pig herd trends

At around the same time, UK producers, unlike those in the rest of the EU, were faced with a ban on the use of stalls and tethers for pregnant sows. This required many to make significant investment in their buildings and also increased production costs. This combination meant that many producers were forced to leave the industry during this period, leading to a rapid decline in the herd, as illustrated in Figure 1. This was exacerbated by outbreaks of Classical Swine Fever (2000) and Foot and Mouth Disease (2001), which led to significant culling of animals and resulted in more producers leaving the industry.

Although pig producers elsewhere in the EU also faced low prices during this period, they did not face all the other challenges experienced by UK producers. As a result, the EU industry did not decline in the same way and UK imports of pork and other pig meat products increased rapidly, as illustrated in Figure 2. The UK was over 0.80 self-sufficient in pig meat in the late-1990s, with most imports being back bacon, for which UK demand exceeded supply, or pork for curing into bacon. By 2003, self-sufficiency had fallen below half and only rose back above that mark in 2010. By 2014, it had increased to 0.55. Pork exports collapsed after the Foot and Mouth Disease outbreak in 2001 and have only gradually recovered since then.

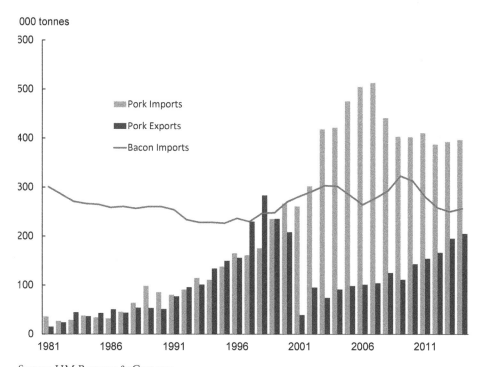

Source: HM Revenue & Customs
Figure 2. Trends in UK trade in pork and bacon

In effect, the UK had exported a significant proportion of its pig production to other EU countries. Today around 0.60 of pig meat consumed in the UK is imported, with around a quarter of domestic production exported. These exports are largely made up of cuts for which there is limited consumer demand on the UK market (e.g. bellies, shoulders, heads, tails and trotters). Imports consist mainly of cuts where there is more demand than can be satisfied from domestic production (mainly cuts and products from the loin and leg, including bacon and ham).

Despite sow numbers being stable or falling in recent years, UK pig meat production has been rising over the last decade. In 2014, output reached 863,000 tonnes, the highest since 2000 and nearly a quarter higher than the low point in 2006. Two factors have combined to drive this trend. First, carcase weights have been rising as improved genetics and nutrition, among other things, have allowed pigs to reach heavier weights without becoming too fat. In the 1980s, average carcase weights were between 60 and 65kg (equivalent to a live weight of around 80-85kg). By the turn of the century, this had risen to 70kg and in 2014, the average weight topped 80kg for the first time (equivalent to around 105kg live weight).

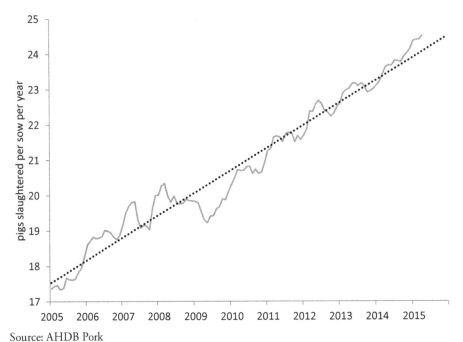

Source: AHDB Pork
Figure 3. UK sow herd productivity

The other factor is the improved productivity of the sow herd. As Figure 3 shows, the number of pigs finished per sow per year has risen from below 18 in 2005 to nearly 25 now. Again, genetics and nutrition have contributed to this increase, along with improved stockmanship and management and fewer disease issues due, in part, to better biosecurity on farm.

UK pig production today

Defra figures from the 2013 June Agricultural Survey show a small fall in the number of UK commercial agricultural holdings with pigs between June 2012 and June 2013, to 11,000. However, within this total, there was an increase in the number of holdings with 1,000 or more pigs, which numbered 1,420, about 60 up on a year before. Between them, these farms accounted for 0.85 of the UK herd. There was also a drop in the number of farms with breeding pigs, which fell slightly to just under 6,000. Again, the vast majority of the herd was located on a small proportion of this total, with 810 farms with 100 or more sows accounting for 0.88 of the national breeding herd (see figure 3). The number of holdings with feeding pigs was almost unchanged at 9,200, with around 4,200 of these also having breeding pigs.

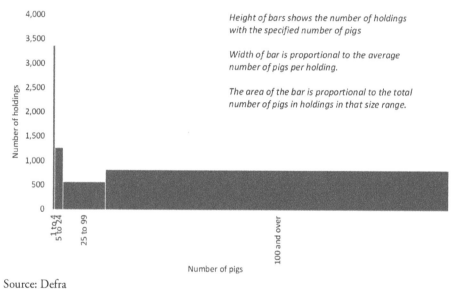

Source: Defra

Figure 4. Number and size of farm holdings with breeding pigs

The numbers above include many holdings which keep pigs but which are also engaged in other agricultural activities. When holdings were classified based on their predominant activity (over two-thirds of output) there were 5,600 specialist pig holdings in the UK in 2010 (the latest year for which UK-wide figures are available). In England, there were 1,826 specialist pig farms in 2013, around 200 more than in 2010. These holdings accounted for over three-quarters of pigs on commercial holdings in England. The 1,200 specialist pig holdings with sows had an average of just over 300 breeding pigs. Pig holdings with feeding pigs had an average of 1,630 animals.

Pig producers are highly geographically concentrated. Of the 4.5 million pigs in the UK, more than 0.80 are in England, with just over 0.1 in Northern Ireland, 0.07 in Scotland and less than 0.01 in Wales. In 2013, well over half of England's pigs were concentrated in just four counties: Norfolk, Suffolk and North and East Yorkshire. It is no coincidence that these areas are major producers of the crops which are the main ingredients of pig feed. As we will see in section 2, feed accounts for the majority of pig production costs, so it makes sense to locate production close to the source of feed, thereby minimising transport costs. There are also significant concentrations of pigs in the South West of England, the Thames Valley, Northern Ireland to the South & East of Lough Neagh and the East of Scotland.

Detailed figures are available on the workforce in England's 1,800 specialist pig farms, although not for the rest of the UK. At that time, they employed a total of 6,000 workers, an average of 3.3 per holding. Just over half of workers on specialist pig farms were farmers, partners, directors and spouses, working either full-time or part-time. Just under a third were regular full-time workers. The remainder were made up of managers, part-time and casual workers.

The number of people working with pigs on non-specialist pig farms is unknown. However, estimates put the total amount of work with pigs at the equivalent of 3,000-4,500 full-time workers (depending on how this is defined). In reality, the workforce will be significantly higher than this, as many of them will work part-time or will only devote part of their time to pig production.

Pig production methods

In England, around 0.40 of the commercial pig breeding herd is kept outdoors. This outdoor production is virtually unique to the UK. Outdoor production on this scale is a relatively new development, having expanded from the late-1990s in response to the stall and tether ban before stabilising in recent years. Its existence is largely due to consumers' preference for outdoor-bred pork as it is perceived to be better for the welfare of the pigs. The UK climate is also relatively conducive to outdoor production, given the general lack of temperature extremes. However, there is only a certain amount of suitable land available and consumer demand for premium products is also limited. This means further expansion of outdoor production beyond current levels is unlikely.

The remaining sows and gilts are kept in indoor systems but here there are differences across the breeding cycle. During farrowing and lactation, most are kept in traditional farrowing crates on fully or partly slatted floors. There is increasing pressure to phase out use of these systems on animal welfare grounds, although alternatives generally involve increased piglet mortality. Various approaches to 'freedom farrowing' systems, which allow the sow to move and turn around while minimising morality rates, are being developed.

For the remainder of the breeding cycle, most indoor sows are kept on straw-based systems. All pregnant sows are kept in groups throughout their gestation period.

Outdoor breeding pigs are typically housed at a density of around 15 sows/gilts per hectare. In most cases, outdoor pigs are used as part of a field rotation system, with pigs spending an average of 17 months in a paddock before they are rotated. Most outdoor producers provide pig arcs for shelter, with some using cabins or tents as well as or instead of arcs.

Once piglets have been weaned, they are less likely to be kept outdoors. Only around one in five weaners (between 7 and 30kg) are housed outdoors, with stocking densities much higher than for breeding pigs, typically close to 400 per hectare. Where weaners are housed indoors, over half are on straw with the remainder mainly on fully-slatted floors.

At later stages in the feeding process, pigs are much less likely to be housed outdoors. Less than one in twenty commercial growing pigs (between 30 and 65kg) and finishers (over 65kg) are kept outdoors, although these figures are likely to be higher for smaller producers. Most of these are kept by a few large-scale free range producers or by a larger number of organic producers, which are mainly small. The majority of feeding pigs which are housed indoors are on straw, a proportion which has increased in recent years. Finishers are more likely to be on slatted floors than growers.

UK pig production in context

The impact of the decline in the UK pig herd is emphasised by the fact that it is now only the tenth largest herd among EU member states (Table 2). Overall, there are 147 million pigs in the EU, meaning that the UK only accounts for around 0.03 of the total. The two largest herds are in Germany and Spain, each of which has over 25 million pigs. A further four countries have more than 10 million pigs, over twice as many as the UK, these being France, Poland, the Netherlands and Denmark. The latter, in particular has a very large industry in proportion to its population and is one of the world's major pig meat exporters (and the leading supplier of imported pork and bacon to the UK).

The EU pig herd has declined in recent years. In part this is because of the gradual reduction of traditional small and mixed farms, particularly in the newer member states in the East, which were not able to compete in the EU market. As a result, pig production has become more of a specialised activity, with fewer, larger farms involved. However, profitability has been challenging for producers across Europe in recent years and has led to some choosing to leave the industry or change their production methods.

While the productivity of the UK sow herd has improved in recent years, it is still some way behind the performance of the best in Europe. Based on comparative

Table 2. Pig numbers in selected EU member states, December

Million Head	2005	2010	2013	2014
EU Total	159.9	152.4	146.2	148.3
Germany	27.0	26.9	28.1	28.3
Spain	24.9	25.7	25.5	26.6
France	15.1	14.3	13.4	13.3
Denmark	12.6	12.3	12.4	12.7
Netherlands	11.0	12.2	12.0	12.1
Poland	18.7	14.8	11.0	11.3
Italy	9.2	9.3	8.6	8.7
Belgium	6.3	6.2	6.4	6.4
Romania	6.6	5.4	5.2	5.0
UK	4.7	4.4	4.4	4.5
Others	23.8	20.9	19.3	19.5

Source: Eurostat

figures from 2013, the latest available, GB producers finished nearly six pigs fewer per sow than their counterparts in Denmark. In part this is because the productivity of outdoor sows is lower than those kept indoors. However, even when the figures are restricted to indoor sows, GB productivity is still well behind. Pigs are also generally finished at lighter weights in the UK than in much of the rest of the EU.

The lower productivity of the GB herd and the lighter carcase weights mean that pig meat production costs are typically among the highest in Europe. However, this is compensated by a price premium which UK producers normally enjoy. Since the late-1990s, UK pig prices have typically been around 10p/kg higher than the EU average. Until the last two years, the premium was normally in the range from 0-20p/kg, with only short periods when it was outside that range. Since the horse meat revelations which hit the UK meat industry in 2013, however, the UK premium has increased as major retailers have focused on sourcing more product from British pigs. In the last year, UK prices have averaged around 30p/kg higher than the EU average.

Looking further afield, the EU has around 0.16 of the world's 1 billion pigs. Nearly half of the total is in China, by far the world's leading pork market. The EU is also one of the main exporters into the world market, along with the US, Canada and Brazil.

Future prospects

As described in section 1.1, the UK pig herd has been broadly stable over the last decade, with a slight decline in the breeding herd offset by improved productivity. There are a number of reasons for thinking that this will continue to be the most likely trend in the coming years.

For any significant expansion to be likely, producers would need to be making sufficient money and have enough confidence to invest in new buildings or equipment. In reality, producers have struggled for profitability over many years. Figure 6 shows that, when depreciation of fixed assets and financing costs are taken into account, producers have only made significant profits in two of the last 13 years. In fact, 2014 was one of those two years, with pig prices at near-record levels at the start of the year and costs at their lowest level for four years. However, pig prices fell rapidly during the second half of 2014 and by the turn of the year producers were, on average, back in the red. With expectations that pig prices will remain subdued for the remainder of 2015, it is unlikely that it will add to the short list of years when pig production was truly profitable.

It is worth noting that, since the production costs in Figure 6 include depreciation, they do not reflect the operating profit/loss of producers. This is how producers have been able to continue in business despite apparently losing so much money. Nevertheless, it also explains why any investment has been limited; a recent study found that over half of pig buildings were more than 20 years old, which must be affecting the productivity of the national herd.

Feed accounts for between 0.60 and 0.70 of total production costs for pigs, meaning that profitability is highly dependent on developments in the feed market. Given the increasing volatility of global cereal and oilseed prices, this creates uncertainty for pig producers and limits their appetite for investment even when they are making money, as in 2014. This explains why there was no expansion in the breeding herd last year.

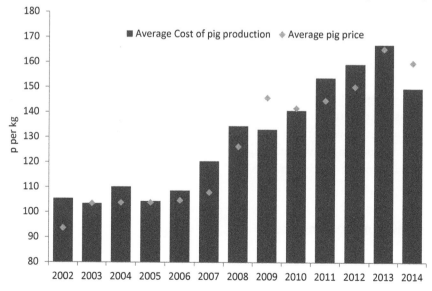

Source: AHDB Pork

Figure 5. GB cost of pig production compared with pig prices

Feed price volatility is not the only risk which will be playing on the mind of producers. Disease threats have also been prominent over the last two years. Two major outbreaks have dominated the global market since early 2014 – African Swine Fever (ASF) in Eastern Europe and Porcine Epidemic Diarrhoea Virus (PEDv) in North America and several Asian countries. Neither has reached the UK yet but if either does it could have a dramatic effect on the industry. ASF, in particular, would mean the closure of export markets and could mean a loss of up to a third in the output of the sector.

A final issue which is likely to limit expansion is UK consumers' preference for certain cuts. Many of the most popular pork products come from either the loin (chops, steaks, back bacon) or leg (roasting joints, gammon, ham). As a result, the UK is estimated to eat around 23 million pigs worth of loins and 19 million pigs worth of legs. This compares with around 11 million UK pigs slaughtered each year. However, for most other parts of the carcase, UK demand is lower – just 6 million pigs worth of shoulder, for example, and much less than this for most other cuts.

Markets need to be found for these other cuts, normally for export, but these are inevitably relatively low value. While expanding production would provide more loins and legs, reducing the requirement to import these cuts, it would also mean that markets would need to be found for more of the lower-value cuts. This would probably mean that the total price for which the parts of a carcase could be sold for would be lower than at present. In turn, this would be likely to reduce returns to producers to a point where further expansion would be discouraged.

Although all of the factors outlined above suggest there is unlikely to be a dramatic expansion of the UK herd, none of them is likely to mean the herd contracts (at least unless the risk of a disease outbreak or major feed price rise becomes reality). However, even if the herd does remain broadly stable, the long-term trends for increasing carcase weights and improved sow productivity should continue. Both trends have been consistent, both in direction and scale, for many years and comparisons with other countries show that there is still plenty of room for improvement. Therefore, pig meat production growth should continue for some time to come, although there may be variations from year to year.

The UK pig feed market

Pig feed today

A variety of different types of feed are used by pig producers. All contain a mix of components designed to provide all of the nutrients required by pigs. Different mixes are used for pigs at different stages of their life cycle. Major components of feed in the UK include cereals (mainly wheat, barley or distillery by-products) and oilseed cake and meal (mainly soya or rape). A wide variety of other ingredients are used less frequently. Just over half of producers report that they home mix some or all of the feed they use. Others buy in ready mixed feed.

There are three main forms of feed used by pig producers: pellets, meal and wet feed. Pellets are the commonest form for all stages of the lifecycle. They are used by around 0.80 of producers to feed weaners, about 0.60 for rearers and finishers and about 0.40 for sows. Meal is used by around 0.3 of producers to feed rearers, finishers and sows but only 0.1 for weaners. Wet feed is most frequently used to feed finishers, with around 0.2 of producers using it. For sows, it is only used in 0.10 of cases and for weaners even less. A small number of producers use other feeding approaches.

During 2014, just over 1.8 million tonnes of compound pig feed were produced in the UK, the highest output since 2001. Nearly half of this was finisher feed, just under 0.25 was sow feed and about 0.20 was grower feed. The remainder was made up of feed for piglets and early growers, along with protein concentrates. The rise was mostly due to higher production of finisher feed, reflecting the increased number of finished pigs and their heavier weights.

With pigs being finished at heavier and heavier weights, if feed efficiency was consistent, it would mean that the Feed Conversion Ratio (FCR) should rise, as heavier pigs convert feed less effectively. However, they also tend to put on more weight, so daily liveweight gains (DLG) would be expected to increase, although this would depend on the amount of feed they are provided with. Between 1997 and about 2010, this is the pattern observed for finishers. However, since then there are signs that the average FCR has started to fall again, indicating some improvement in feed efficiency. At the same time, DLG has levelled off, suggesting that similar growth rates may be being achieved with less feed.

The recent apparent improvements in feed efficiency have probably been driven by an increased focus on managing costs, given the rapid fluctuations in feed prices recorded in recent years. Having spent most of the decade up to 2007 below £100 per tonne, UK feed wheat prices have since experienced three separate periods when they have reached or exceeded £200 per tonne. Although prices are currently back to being closer to the £100 mark, the threat of further price spikes is ever present.

Nevertheless, while producers are doing what they can to improve feed efficiency, many are still using the same feeding systems which they have been using for many years. Many of these are sub-optimal, to say the least, with many potential problems. Some systems will involve significant amounts of waste, a particular problem outdoors. Others could mean some pigs in a pen getting too much food while others go hungry, while the availability of the right amount of water can also be an issue.

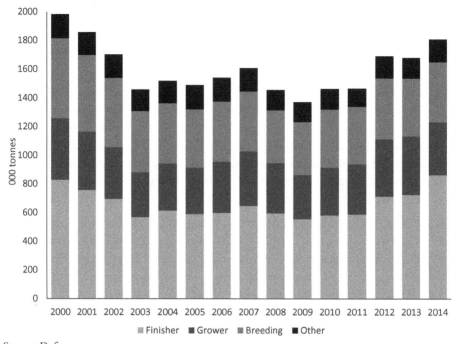

Source: Defra

Figure 6. UK compound pig feed production

This is partly the result of the poor profitability of the industry over many years, which has limited investment in buildings and equipment.

As well as costing money through inefficient use of expensive feed, inadequate feeding systems can cause other problems too. This is particularly true for sows and gilts for breeding, where nutrition has an important role to play in determining the size and uniformity of litters and the rate at which they grow, both pre- and post-weaning. If finishing pigs grow at different rates because the amount and type of feed is not right for them as individuals, it can cause some to be overweight or overfat at slaughter, while others are underweight. Even ignoring factors like this, for outdoor producers, compaction of the ground by the equipment used to distribute feed can cause environmental problems, while maintenance of outdated equipment can be another unwelcome cost.

Pig feed tomorrow

For these and other reasons, there has been increasing investment in finding ways of feeding pigs more efficiently and effectively. From producers' point of view, the key

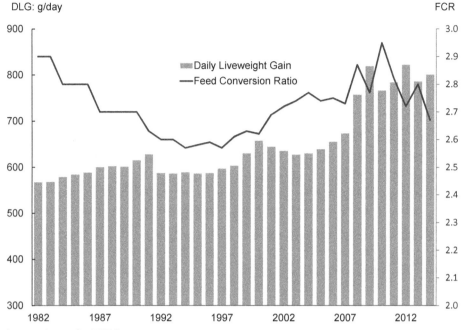

DLG: g/day   FCR

Source: Agrosoft, AHDB

Figure 7. Feed efficiency of GB finishing pigs

driver is inevitably to reduce the costs associated with feeding. This needs to be done in a way which ensures that pigs are still receiving the most appropriate feed for their stage of production, whether they are kept indoors or outdoors. Getting it right will bring other benefits though, in areas such as animal welfare, environmental impact and eating quality of the end product. This is why feed-related areas are prominent among the priorities which the industry has identified for on-farm trials.

Much of the research is around better targeting of feed to the requirements of individual pigs or at least groups of pigs. Getting this right means more measurement of performance, for example through regular weighing of individuals or groups of pigs. While doing this manually can be difficult and disruptive, there are now options for automatic weighing which are much less intrusive and make it easier to spot problems at an earlier stage.

From a group point of view, targeting means ensuring that the feed being provided at each stage of the production cycle is tailored to the nutritional requirements at that time. This may mean use of a range of different compound feeds or mixes during the cycle, rather than generic 'sow feed' or 'finisher feed'. However, it could be as simple as making sure that the amount of feeder and drinker space is optimised so that all pigs in the group can access the right amount of food, not just the more dominant animals.

Going beyond this, new technologies offer improved opportunities for targeting feeding at individual pigs. This can be done using electronic tags, for example, the cost of which is reducing. This can allow feed intake to be monitored on an individual basis, allowing the right amount to be delivered to each pig. Ear tags can also be used to enable more data to be held about the performance of individual growing pigs, allowing growth to be monitored and the impact of interventions to be assessed.

Much of the targeted feeding technology is currently focused on breeding pigs, with approaches to both indoor and outdoor sows. Although there are significant set-up costs, most trials suggest that costs can be recovered fairly quickly in reduced feed costs, without even taking account of any performance improvement.

Alongside the trials of new technology, new research is focusing on how to feed to achieve optimal performance. Current examples include the effect of the amount of space each feeding pig has on its growth and the impact that feeder space has on performance. Work is also being undertaken on the impact of sow body condition and feed intake during lactation on subsequent performance of both the sow and her piglets.

Some of the trials and research could have fairly immediate impacts on feed efficiency. However, using feed efficiently isn't the only way for producers to cut feed costs. The other is to reduce the price of feed. To some extent this can be done by using some form of risk management, for example by buying some feed ahead, or by varying delivery sizes or frequencies. It can also be done by altering the blend of existing ingredients being used but there is a limit to how much this can be done without losing too much nutritional value. Therefore, another area of development is the search for new raw materials to form part of pig rations.

This is nothing new. Producers have been using by-products from various manufacturing processes as part of pig feed for many years and their use has increased over time. Their use, though, can be limited by the amount which is available and by the lack of consistency of the products. This means that the search for new feed ingredients is intensifying, with concerns about the environmental impact of soyabean production contributing. This means that much of the current focus is on finding alternative sources for the protein component of feed, much of which is currently provided by soya meal, most of which is imported from Brazil.

Among the options being examined are home-grown crops such as peas and beans, long used in animal feed but difficult to make economically viable and consistent enough. However, more radical options are also being considered, such as the resumption of use of Processed Animal Protein (e.g. meat and bone meal, fish meal) or even using insect protein. Insects are farmed successfully in other parts of the world and could be an option here too – after all, pigs are omnivores. It is worth noting, though, that even if nutritional and economic issues can be resolved with these options, there will still be work required to convince consumers that they are acceptable.

These are just some examples of where new technology or new approaches could alter the pig feed market in the years ahead. Plenty of other ideas are also being talked about, even the use of drones to deliver feed to outdoor pigs – perhaps the perfect solution to avoiding soil compaction, although probably some way off becoming a reality.

What is clear is that the pig industry is open to new ideas and there are opportunities available for those who can find ways to reduce costs or improve the effectiveness of feeding. This suggests that, even if, as expected, there is no dramatic change in the size of the UK pig herd in the coming years, there could still be plenty of change in how and what those pigs are fed.

LIST OF PARTICIPANTS

The forty-seventh University of Nottingham Feed Conference was organised by the following committee:

MR A. ARMSTRONG (*Kemin UK*)
MR M. HAZZLEDINE (*Premier Nutrition*)
MR R. KIRKLAND (*Volac International*)
DR M.A. VARLEY (*The Pig Technology Company*)
DR P. WILCOCK (*ABVista USA*)
DR K. WONNACOTT (*ForFarmers UK*)

DR J.M. BRAMELD
PROF P.C. GARNSWORTHY (*Secretary*)
DR N. KENDALL
DR T. PARR   *University of Nottingham*
PROF A.M. SALTER
DR K.D. SINCLAIR
PROF J. WISEMAN (*Chairman*)

The conference was held at the University of Nottingham Sutton Bonington Campus, 23rd - 24th June 2015. The following persons registered for the meeting:

Allen, Mrs D	QNM Limited, 46A Mudford Road, Yeovil, Somerset BA21 4AB, UK
Ander, Dr L	Centre for Environmental Geochemistry, British Geological Survey, Keyworth, Nottingham NG12 5GG, UK
Archer, Dr S	University of Nottingham, Sutton Bonington Campus, Loughborough LE12 5RD, UK
Armstrong, Mr A	Kemin UK Limited, Tudor House, Hampton Road, Southport, Merseyside , UK
Bardsley, Mr M	Three Rivers Veterinary Group, London Road, Beccles, Suffolk NR34 9YU, UK
Bartram, Mr C	Mole Valley Farmers, Exmoor House, Lime Way, Pathfields Business Park, South Molton, Devon EX36 3LH, UK
Bollwein, Prof H	University of Zurich, Clinic of Reproductive Medicine, Vetsuisse-Faculty , Switzerland
Bone, Mr P	Ruminant Mineral Consulting Ltd. 39 Stratton Heights, Cirencester GL7 2RH, UK
Brassington, Miss A	The University of Nottingham, Sutton Bonington Campus, Loughborough LE12 5RD, UK
Calsamiglia, Dr S	University of Barcelona, Fac Vet, Edifici 5, Bellaterra 08193, Spain
Connerton, Prof I	The University of Nottingham, Sutton Bonington Campus, Loughborough LE12 5RD, UK
Dakheel, Mr M	University of Reading, 1 Earley Gate, Building TOB1, Spur D, Reading, Berkshire RG6 6AT, UK
Dunshea, Prof F	The University of Melbourne, Faculty of Veterinary & Agricultural Sciences, Parkville Victoria 3010, Australia
Garnsworthy, Prof P C	University of Nottingham, Sutton Bonington Campus, Loughborough, Leics LE12 5RD, UK
Glen, Mr T	AB Agri Ltd, 64 Innovation Way, Peterborough, Cambs. PE2 6FL, UK

Goatman, Mr T	AHDB, Stoneleigh Park, Kenilworth, Warwickshire CV8 2TL, UK
Goodman, Miss J	University of Nottingham, Sutton Bonington Campus, Loughborough, Leics LE12 5RD, UK
Graham, Mr M	Tremywawr, Breidden Ave, Arddleen, Llanymynech, Powys SY22 6SP, UK
Holder, Mr P	ED & F Man Liquid Products, Alexandra House, Regent Road, Bootle L20 1ES, UK
Homer, Dr E	University of Nottingham, Sutton Bonington Campus, Loughborough, Leics LE12 5RD, UK
Howarth, Mr S	Agriculture & Horticulture Development Board, Stoneleigh Park, Kenilworth CV8 2TL, UK
Hulland, Mrs C	NWF Agriculture Ltd, Wardle, Cheshire CW5 6AQ, UK
Hurdidge, Mr L	Lallemand Animal Nutrition UK Ltd, 11-13 Spring Lane North, Malvern Link, Worcestershire WR14 1BU, UK
Jacklin, Mr D	Ruminant Nutrition Consultancy, 10 Station Close, Riding Mill, Northumberland NE44 6HE, UK
Kasprzak, Dr M	University of Nottingham, Sutton Bonington Campus, Loughborough, Leics LE12 5RD, UK
Kendall, Dr N	University of Nottingham, SVMS, Sutton Bonington Campus, Loughborough LE12 5RD, UK
Kennedy, Dr J	Devenish Nutrition, Lagan House, 19 Clarendon Road, Belfast BT1 3BG, UK
Koopmans, Miss A	Schothorst Feed Research B.V., P.O. Box 533, 8200 AM Lelystad , Netherlands
Lawson, Mrs K	University of Nottingham, Sutton Bonington Campus, Loughborough, Leics LE12 5RD, UK
Macrae, Dr A	DHHPS,The Royal (Dick) School of Veterinary Studie, Roslin Institute, University of Edinburgh, Easter Bush Veterinary Centre, Roslin EH25 9RG, UK
May, Miss B	Premier Nutrition, Brereton Business Park, The Levels, Rugeley WS15 1RD, UK
May, Miss K	University of Nottingham, Sutton Bonington Campus, Loughborough, Leics LE12 5RD, UK
Napier, Prof J	Rothamsted Research, Harpenden, Herts AL5 2JQ, UK
Nichols, Dr S	Trouw Nutrition, Blenheim House, Blenheim Road, Ashbourne, Derbyshire DE6 1HA, UK
Northover, Mrs S	University of Nottingham, Sutton Bonington Campus, Loughborough, Leics LE12 5RD, UK
Packington, Mr A	DSM Nutritional Products Ltd, Heanor Gate, Heanor, Derbyshire DE75 7SG, UK
Parr, Dr T	University of Nottingham, Sutton Bonington Campus, Loughborough, Leics LE12 5RD, UK
Price, Mr M	Wynnstay Group PLC, Eagle House, Llansantffraid, Powys SY22 6AQ, UK
Roberts, Mr G	George Veterinary Group, High Street, Malmesbury SN16 9AY, UK

Rooke, Dr J — SRUC, West Mains Road, Edinburgh EH9 3JG, UK

Ryan, Mr B — Agritech, Ballyanny, Nenagh Co Tipperary, Ireland

Salter, Prof A — University of Nottingham, Sutton Bonington Campus, Loughborough, Leics LE12 5RD, UK

Saunders, Mr N — University of Nottingham, Sutton Bonington Campus, Loughborough, Leics LE12 5RD, UK

Smith, Ms L — Kingshay, Bridge Farm, West Bradley BA6 8LU, UK

Tennant, Miss L — University of Nottingham, Sutton Bonington Campus, Loughborough, Leics LE12 5RD, UK

Thornton, Mr D — Rumenco Ltd, Stretton House, Derby Road, Burton-on-Trent, Staffs. DE13 0DW, UK

Tulley, Mr W — EBVC Ltd, Redhills Lane, Penrith, Cumbria CA11 0DT, UK

Varley, Mr M — The Pig Technology Company, 16 Willow Avenue, Clifford, Wetherby LS23 6LA, UK

Vaughan, Mr I — Wynnstay Group PLC, Eagle House, Llansantffraid, Powys SY22 6AQ, UK

Walk, Miss C — AB Vista Feed Ingredients, 3 Woodstock Court, Blenheim Road, Marlborough, Wiltshire SN8 4AN, UK

Wallace, Mr J — University of Aberdeen, King's College, Aberdeen AB24 3FX, UK

Walling, Dr G — JSR Genetics Ltd, Southburn, Driffield, East Yorkshire YO25 9ED, UK

Wang, Dr TC — Anyou Biotechnology Group Co Ltd, 239 Xingang Road, Taicang City Jiangsu Prov, China

Ware, Mr J — Roquette UK Ltd, 9-11 Sallow Road, Corby NN17 5JX, UK

Webb, Prof R — University of Nottingham, Sutton Bonington Campus, Loughborough LE12 5RD, UK

Whelan, Dr S — Agriculture & Horticulture Development Board, Stoneleigh Park, Kenilworth CV8 2TL, UK

White, Dr G — University of Nottingham, Sutton Bonington Campus, Loughborough, Leics LE12 5RD, UK

Wilde, Mr D — Premier Nutrition, Brereton Business Park, The Levels, Rugeley, Staffordshire WS15 1RD, UK

Williams, Mrs N — Rumenco Ltd, Stretton House, Derby Road, Burton-on-Trent, Staffs. DE13 0DW, UK

Wiseman, Prof J — University of Nottingham, Sutton Bonington Campus, Loughborough LE12 5RD, UK

Woodward, Prof M — The University of Reading, Dept of Food & Nutritional Sciences, PO Box 226, Whiteknights, Reading RG6 6AP,

Index